The ergonomics of workspaces and machines:
A design manual

The ergonomics of workspaces and machines:
A design manual

T. S. Clark and E. N. Corlett

Taylor & Francis
London and Philadelphia
1984

Published 1984 by Taylor & Francis Ltd, 4 John St., London WC1N 2ET
Published in the USA by Taylor & Francis Inc., 242 Cherry St., Philadelphia,
PA 19106-1906

British Library Cataloguing in Publication Data

Clark, T.S.
The ergonomics of workspaces and machines:
   a design manual
1. Work environment   2. Human engineering
3. Man-machine systems
I. Title   II. Corlett, E.N.
725'.4.   T59.77

ISBN 0-85066-246-X

Library of Congress Cataloging in Publication Data

Clark, T.S. (Thomas Stephen)
The ergonomics of workspaces and machines.
   Bibliography: p.
   Includes index.
1. Human engineering.   2. Work environment.
3. Man-machine systems.   4. Design, Industrial.
I. Corlett, E. N. (Esmond Nigel)   II. Title.
III. Title: Ergonomics of work spaces and machines.
T59.7 C57 1984   620.8'2   84-242

ISBN 0-85066-246-X

Typeset by Kempshott Phototypesetting Service, 21a Homesteads Road, Kempshott,
Basingstoke, Hants.

Printed in the UK by Taylor & Francis (Printers) Ltd, Rankine Road, Basingstoke,
Hants.

Contents

Foreword

The importance of good product design is clear. Apart from the improvement to the quality of life that can be brought about by products that are easy to use and do their job well, there are important commercial issues that should be noted by any manufacturing company or nation. A product competes in its market according to many different factors including performance, price, appearance, safety, reliability and maintainability; and all of these depend crucially upon the design of the product. Good product design and economic success are thus closely linked.

One such factor that is immediately important to the owner or operator is 'ease of use'. Displays that cannot be seen or understood and controls that are awkward or even impossible to use are painfully obvious at the point of sale (or no sale!) and it is strange that such deficiencies should be so common. If the user can perceive such defects so clearly, how was it that the designer was so blind?

It might require an entire treatise to consider this paradox properly, but what is clear is that many designers require better guidance on ergonomics, and in this regard the following text will be of considerable value. I wish both it and its readers all success.

Keith Grant
Director, The Design Council

Preface

Every industrial system consists of some or all of the following components: hardware (the physical aspects), software (non-physical aspects), the physical environment and the organization. An objective of the designer is to arrange these components to give a harmonious and efficient operation. An objective of ergonomics is to match, or provide the information to match, the various other parts of the system to the characteristics and abilities of the people involved in it. By utilizing ergonomics the designer's opportunities to create a system which reliably achieves its functions are improved.

This manual is for a wide range of designers but emphasizes data of particular interest to those concerned with workspaces, working equipment and machines. These may be in factories, offices, warehouses, etc. The information is laid out in the sequence in which the designer will most probably require it, starting with a brief introduction, an illustration of the range of data and their interactions with each other, and a check list for preliminary design decisions. The sections which follow are on workspace design including environment design, design of manual controls, and design of displays and information. They are cross-referenced and supported by a detailed index and references to other texts.

It should be noted that a very important design requirement is a specification, or brief. The lack of usability of much in the industrial, business and consumer world arises because the designer's instructions have not specified criteria for usability. This manual has been laid out so that the customer for a product or workplace may also specify the ergonomic requirements. In particular, the Ergonomics Check Chart on pp. 6 – 10 lists briefly the requirements appropriate for such a specification and is designed to assist in the clear specifications of human requirements in a form in which the designer can satisfy them.

The Summary of Contents which follows this preface will provide an overview of the manual and demonstrates its structure and sequence, from which the user may recognize the purposes of each chapter. These chapter summaries are repeated at the start of each chapter, to assist the user in quickly locating his desired point while keeping in mind the overall structure and interactions in the design process.

References, and a bibliography for further reading, are given, but the gradual development of an ergonomics viewpoint and expertise in ergonomics applications will be aided by the introduction into the design office of an ergonomics journal and association with an ergonomics society. The wide applications of the subject, and its contributions to the many aspects of product and workplace, will be better recognized and incorporated by this continuous exposure to its developing applications in business and industry.

Summary of Contents

This *Summary of Contents* is intended to give the user an overview of the Manual, so that he/she may recognize the range of subjects covered, and the sequence in which they are presented. This sequence approximates to the general sequence of design and the sequence in which the various subjects would be considered. Particular subject areas can also be identified from this summary. To assist the user to retain the structure of the manual, each chapter summary is repeated at the beginning of its chapter. The numbered sub-headings of the summary also represent the chapter sub-headings.

2. WORKSPACE DESIGN

3. ENVIRONMENTAL DESIGN

1. Introduction

1

1.1. Introduction to the ergonomics of machines

1.1.1. Definition

Ergonomics can be defined as the study of human abilities and characteristics which affect the design of equipment, systems and jobs.
It is an interdisciplinary activity based on engineering, psychology, anatomy and physiology and its aims are to improve efficiency, safety and operator well-being.

1.1.2. Content

Every industrial system consists of some or all of the following components, each of which interacts with the others and with technical, economic and other considerations and constraints. Ergonomics is concerned with the interfaces and interactions between the human operator(s) and the other components and with the effects of these interactions on system performance.

Figure 1. Chart of the interactions in the industrial system.

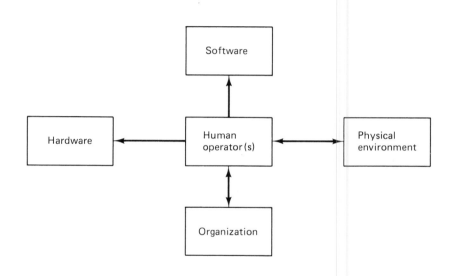

Table 1. Components of the industrial system.

Component	Design areas	Considerations, constraints
Hardware	Design and layout of components	Process, equipment
Human Operator(s)	Physical characteristics, abilities, etc.	Body size Strength, work capacity Posture Fatigue and endurance
	Information reception and processing	Senses (vision, audition, etc.) Attention Memory, etc.
	Individual and social characteristics	Age, sex, background, race Skill, training Motivation Job satisfaction and interest Boredom Attitudes, etc.
Software	Error-free performance	Standard operating procedures Instructions Manuals Symbols, etc.
Physical Environment	Safe performance	Temperature Noise Lighting Vibration Atmosphere and ventilation, etc.
Organization	Organization of personnel/production	Work — rest schedules, Pacing, cycle time Shift work Job content Interest Satisfaction Responsibility Social interaction, etc.

1.1.3. Ergonomics considerations in machine tool design

Figure 2. Ergonomics considerations in machine tool design.

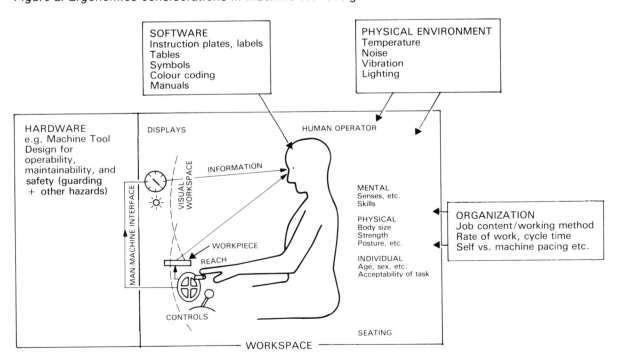

1.2. Main considerations in the application of ergonomics

1.2.1. Important considerations

Good ergonomics design should be regarded as an essential part of good design, not as something separate.

Ergonomics implications should be considered at ALL stages of the design process, especially the early stages.
All design decisions are likely to have some implications for operators or maintenance personnel. It is not sufficient only to consider ergonomics in the final detail stage when all major design decisions have been made.

Ergonomics implications should be considered and discussed by all concerned with or affected by a design.
Co-operation is needed between members of a design team and between designers and the client's production department, personnel, etc. The comments of operators are particularly valuable.

Ergonomics requirements should be included in the brief or specification so that their consideration is ensured.
Requirements should be as specific as possible or they may not be adequately considered. If necessary, ergonomics requirements should be budgeted for (e.g., design time, trials, etc).

There are few simple rules in ergonomics but there are often limits beyond which performance or safety is likely to deteriorate.
Most design decisions involve compromises. If an optimal ergonomics solution is not possible the consequences should be carefully considered, especially if limits are exceeded.

Ergonomics data should be applied intelligently and with caution.
In applying any data care is needed to ensure that the data are applicable to the problem in hand. The origins and assumptions of any data should be examined.

For more difficult problems, where a logical approach alone is insufficient, or where the consequences of error are serious, ergonomics specialists should be consulted.

Mock-ups and prototype trials are important for confirmation.
Using ergonomics information is likely to result in a better first approximation and ultimate design. However, the use of mock-ups, even simple ones, with representative users is valuable for confirming details of fit, reach, layout, etc.

1.2.2. Suggested procedure

Figure 3. *A suggested iterative approach to design.*

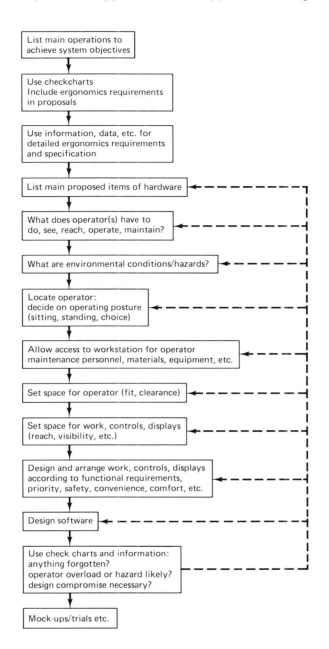

1.3. Ergonomics check chart

The considerations given in the chart should be satisfied if a design is to be ergonomic.

This chart should be used in preliminary design for preparing the brief or list of general requirements; also it should be used during the design process for checking that nothing has been forgotten.

This chart provides general statements relating to some of the main interactions or considerations indicated in the *Interaction Matrix* (p.11). Of the design and performance factors listed, functional requirements, safety, operability, size and maintainability are presented in this chart. Other factors can be included as required, depending on the system being designed.

Design and performance factors (and ergonomics factors) are interrelated. The separation of factors in this chart is to simplify analysis and classification. It is not implied that they should be treated separately in design. In particular, safety should be treated as a part of design, not as something separate or as an afterthought.

Table 2. Check chart of design and performance factors and ergonomic considerations.

Design and performance factors	Ergonomics considerations	Page
Functional requirements	Assign functions to hardware and operator(s) according to abilities and characteristics of users besides technical, economic and other considerations.	5
Safety		
General	Refer to appropriate regulations and standards, etc.	91 – 92
	Remove hazard at source if possible	59
	or provide barrier (e.g., guard) or separation	35 – 37
	or provide personal protection.	46
	Separate and/or protect from mechanical, electrical, chemical or other hazards.	35 – 37
	Separate and/or protect from extremes of temperature, noise, vibration and other environmental hazards.	41 – 48
	Minimize physical, mental and environmental fatigue or stress.	
Physical workspace	Design working position and task to avoid strain and damage to the body, especially the back.	14 – 29
	Components and materials to be safely handled, manually or mechanically.	33
	Locate hazards beyond longest reach.	35 – 36
	Openings to be small enough to prevent access to hazards.	36 – 37
	Provide space for access and emergency exit.	32
	Minimize obstruction to physical action and vision.	

Design and performance factors	Ergonomics considerations	Page
Control design	Choose and design controls for safe and efficient operation, considering requirements for force, speed, accuracy, feedback, etc.	52 – 60
	Design to avoid accidental operation.	55 – 58
	Locate to avoid interference.	53 – 54
	Locate controls for safe, efficient and comfortable operation considering priority, frequency and duration of operation, speed, accuracy and sequence. Locate emergency controls suitably.	53 – 58
	Controls should move in a direction compatible with display or system movement.	59 – 61
Display design	Choose, design and locate displays for safe and efficient operation considering operational requirements, type of information presented and what is to be done with the information.	64 – 67
	Avoid masking (interference) of communication warnings. Provide clear warnings, labels, instructions, manuals, etc.	25 – 39
Operability		
Body size	Allow range of users to fit work station and reach work and controls.	19 – 21
	Note variations with sex, ethnic background, etc.	20
Posture	Avoid fatiguing posture except for infrequent, short duration tasks.	14
	Allow changes of posture.	15, 16
	Provide support (seating, handle, rails, arm rests, foot rests, work tops, etc.) where possible.	16
Movement	Design for efficient handling (sequence, etc.).	14
	Avoid static muscular work. Balance muscle groups (e.g., two-arm operation).	16
Strength	Design for variation (e.g., sex differences) and weakest proposed user.	33 – 34
	Choose limb or muscle group appropriate to the task. Consider maximum vs. continuous effort.	14, 17
	Consider location, magnitude, direction, distance, frequency and duration of forces.	53, 55 – 59

Design and performance factors	Ergonomics considerations	Page
	Use power assistance where appropriate.	
Work capacity/rate	Allow adequate rest pauses or change of task. Machine-paced tasks (work rate determined by machine) to be avoided. Provide buffer storage. Allow for effects of physical environment (temperature, noise, lighting, vibration) on work capacity.	
Visibility	Allow comfortable viewing posture.	17, 25
	No visual obstructions: eye positions of users.	17, 25
	Objects of suitable size vs. viewing distance.	17, 25
	Allow for visual defects spectacles, colour defects.	17
Illumination	Provide adequate illumination for task: general background, local, in-built.	18, 19
	Design for poorest lighting conditions: brightness, shadow.	
	Provide adequate contrast between object and background: lighting, colour, size, shape.	48
	Avoid glare by position and design of lighting, work surfaces, material.	49
	Colours to be appropriate for task, safety, aesthetics.	50, 72
Choice and design of controls	Select and design controls according to functional requirements.	52, 53, 55 − 61
Layout of controls	Arrange work and controls according to priority, functional requirements and comfort: consider the importance for safety, frequency, duration, force, speed, accuracy, sequence and compatibility between controls and displays.	53 − 54, 59 − 61
Visual displays, information, software	Select and design according to functional requirements, standards, etc.	64 − 67
Layout of visual task and displays	Arrange according to functional requirements for priority, convenience, comfort, importance for attention, frequency, sequence, etc.	67 − 68
Noise, auditory signals	Auditory signals/displays to gain attention.	73 − 74

Design and performance factors	Ergonomics considerations	Page
	Auditory environment should not interfere with communication, warnings, etc., or cause annoyance or distraction.	42, 43
Information load	Avoid overloading capacity to receive and process information, e.g., minimize periods of concentrated attention; allow for reduced memory of older operators.	

Size

Workstation	Choose seated, standing or choice of working position.	14 – 15
	Allow for *range* of users to: fit workstation, reach work and controls, see work and displays.	19 – 20
	Allow clearances for head, trunk and legs of largest user.	23, 30 – 32
	Allow reaches for arms and legs of smallest user. Adjustment where appropriate.	23 – 28
	Allow comfortable vision: viewing posture, viewing angles, viewing distance.	29
Access	Space/gangways/aisles/ladders to the workstation, for maintenance and as an emergency escape.	30 – 32
Equipment	Portable equipment, tools and protective equipment to be appropriate for users, tasks and space.	
	Controls, displays, seating, etc. to be of recommended sizes.	55 – 59, 68 – 89
Components	Convenient size and weight for handling in installation, operation or maintenance. Modular construction where possible. Mechanical handling where appropriate. Objects to be of suitable size for viewing in worst conditions or use viewing aids.	33 – 34

Maintainability

Access	Provide access to all parts for maintenance. Allow priority of access according to design life, probability and consequences of failure. Provide warnings of failure. Consider location of repair site, workshop, factory.	30 – 32

Design and performance factors	Ergonomics considerations	Page
Space	Provide space for maintenance task for: maintenance personnel, operating tools, removing components and openings. Provide access to point of repair: walking, climbing, crawling.	15, 17, 30 – 32
Posture	Working posture to be appropriate for nature and duration of task: standing, sitting, kneeling, lying. Avoid interference with other operators.	14, 16
Lifting and handling	Components to be suitable size and weight for manual handling where appropriate. Provide lifting gear and lifting eyes if necessary. Covers, cases, fastenings and connectors to be easily removable and replaceable.	33
Instructions and manuals	Provide instructions, labels and manuals for safe and effective maintenance.	
Physical environment	Allow for environmental conditions and safety of maintenance task — provide protection.	42 – 48

1.4. Interaction matrix

The matrix below (Table 3) shows the main interactions between ergonomics factors and design and operational factors relating to machines. Other factors (e.g., organizational) may be included, depending on the system.

A general interaction between the ergonomics factors may be assumed. The strength of the individual interactions will depend on the system.

Table 3. The main interactions between ergonomics factors and the design and performance factors.

Ergonomics factors	Design and performance factors										
	Functional require-ments	Cost	Size[a]	Operability	Safety	Maintain-ability	Reliability	Manu-factur-ability	Quality control	Market-ability, accept-ability	Aesthetics
General human characteristics											
Human vs. machine operation	●	●	○	●	●	●	●	●	●	●	
User population characteristics (age, sex, background, toleration)	○	○	●	○	●	●		●	●	●	○
Skills, selection, training	●	●		●	●	●		●	●	●	
Physical Workspace											
Body-size variation	○	○	●	●	●	●				●	
Reach, clearance and fit	○	○	●	●	●	●				●	
Postural comfort	○		●	●	○	○				○	
Seating design	○		○	○	○					○	
Strength: limits and variations	●			●	●	●				○	
Physical work capacity, endurance	●	○		●	●	○	○			○	○
Control design	○	○	○	●	●	○	○				○
Layout of work and controls	○	○	○	●	●	●	○	○	○		○
Visual workspace, display and Information											
Visual abilities and defects	○	○	○	●	●	○			●		
Visual task design	○	○	○	●	●	○	○	○	○	○	
Visual display design	○	○	○	●	●	○	○	○	○	○	○
Layout of visual tasks and displays	○	○	●	●	○	○	○				○
Control – display compatibility	○	○		●	●						
Passive displays (labels, symbols, instructions, manuals)	○	○		●	●	●	○				○
Auditory signals and displays (attention, processing, memory, etc.)	○	○		○	●	○	○				
Information load	●			●	●		○				
Physical Environment											
Lighting (recommended illumination, contrast, colour, glare)	○	○	○	●	●	●	○		●	○	○
Temperature (dry bulb high/low, radiant high/low, humidity, air speed)	○	○	○	●	●	●	○		○	●	
Noise (dangerous levels, masking of signals)	○	○	○	●	●	●	○		○	●	
Vibration (damaging effects, interference)	○	○	○	●	●	●	○		○	●	
Organizational											
Layout and flow of personnel, material and plan	○	●	●	●	○	○					
Rate of work (pacing, buffer stocks, shifts)	○	●		●	○	○			○	●	
Job content	○	●		○	○	○	○			○	
Inspection system	○	●					○		●		

○ = interaction.   ● = strong interaction.

[a]Size refers to the size of the structure, access, workstation or components.

2. Workspace Design

2.1. Design decisions and principles

All main design decisions relating to the physical workspace (posture, access, clearance, size, reach and safety distances) are itemized. For each of these, design principles are given, as well as the appropriate body or other dimensions.

Page 14

2.2. Body-size variations

Data on body-size variation are given to aid the use of available size data or to correct assumptions on workspace design. Data sources are given in the *Bibliography.*

Page 19

2.3. Suggested methods of workspace designs

Workspace limits, when suitable body-size data are available, can be defined using a check-list.
A series of drawings of reach and visual zones are presented for setting out a workspace. They are prepared for the general UK adult population but could be modified for other populations.
The drawings are set out in elevational form on grids, and the workspace zones separated into zones of priority for placing work, controls and displays. Converted into transparent overlays, drawn to appropriate scale, the drawings can be used for quick checks on the drawing board.

Page 21

2.4. Clearance, access, size and safety distance details

Clearance and access dimensions for both seated and standing operators are given in terms of the UK adult population.
Safety distances (i.e., a reach or body dimension plus a safety allowance) are given in detail.

Page 30

2.5. Fitting trials

Mock-up methods for obtaining confirmation of preliminary design decisions, such as simulators, full or abbreviated fitting trials, are outlined.

Page 38

13

2.1. Design decisions and principles

2.1.1. General arrangements

The worker should be able to maintain an upright and forward-facing posture.

Where vision is a requirement of the task, the necessary work points must be adequately visible with the head and trunk upright or with the head inclined slightly forward.

All work activities should permit the worker to adopt several different, but equally healthy and safe, postures without reducing capability to do the work.

Work should be arranged so that it may be done, at the worker's choice, in either a seated or a standing position. When seated the worker should be able to use the back rest of the chair at will, without necessitating a change of working movements.

The weight of the body, when standing, should be carried equally on both feet, and foot pedals should be designed accordingly.

Work should not be performed consistently at or above the level of the heart; even the occasional performance where force is exerted above the heart level should be avoided. Where light hand work must be performed above heart level, rests for the upper arms are a requirement.

Work activities should be performed with the joints at about the mid-point of their range of movement. This applies particularly to the head, trunk and upper limbs.

Where muscular force has to be exerted it should be by the largest appropriate muscle groups available and in a direction co-linear with the limbs concerned.

Where a force has to be exerted repeatedly, it should be possible to exert it with either of the arms, or either of the legs, without adjustment to the equipment.

2.1.2. Working position

Choose the working position according to the following criteria:

Operator's choice
It is preferable to arrange for both sitting and standing.

Sitting
Where a stable body is needed: for accurate control, fine manipulation;
for light manual work (continuous);
for close visual work — with prolonged attention;
for limited headroom, low work heights.
Where foot controls are necessary (unless of infrequent or short duration).

Standing
For heavy, bulky loads.
Where there are frequent moves from the workplace.
Where there is no knee room under the equipment.
Where there is limited front – rear space.
Where there are a large number of controls and diaplays

Support seat
Where there is no room for a normal seat but a support is desirable.

2.1.3. Access

To workstation
To workpoints
For maintenance

Allow space for the largest user(s) and make allowances for equipment, tools, temporary storage of components, etc. Available from the chosen work position while maintaining an upright posture and without excessive arm reach.

Height.
Shoulder width.
Trunk girth.
Hand dimensions.
Arm dimensions.
Aisle, gangway, ladder dimensions.
Size of openings, etc.

2.1.4. Clearance

Vertical
The minimum space between the floor and an overhead obstruction must allow for the largest user plus footwear and headgear (NB roof heights have architectural requirements).

Head height (standing)
Seat/head height (sitting)
Knee clearance (sitting).

Lateral
Design for the largest user plus an allowance for movement and equipment.

Hip width, shoulder width.

Forward
Design for the largest user plus an allowance for movement and equipment. Provide a recess for the foot.

Forward trunk dimension.
Seat-back — worktop dimension.
Foot length.

Hazards	The hazard must be beyond the reach of the longest arm (free reach). The opening size and distance to the hazard from the guards must be such that the hazard cannot be reached by the longest, smallest diameter finger.	Arm length. Shoulder length. Hand, finger dimensions.
Knee-well width	Design for the seat width plus movement	Seat width, hip width.
Knee-well depth	Design for the longest thigh plus stretching the lower leg.	Thigh length, leg length, foot length.
Seat – worktop vertical clearance	Allow for the largest thigh thickness and for raising the knees, if the pedals are high, and crossing legs.	Thigh thickness.

2.1.5. Seating

Adjustability	The seating should be adjustable (vertically/horizontally) if possible.	
Seat width	Design for the largest hip.	Hip width.
Seat length	Design for the shortest thigh.	Thigh length.
Seat height	This depends on the system: work height, need to operate pedals, etc. If the height is fixed, then design so that the shortest lower legs can reach the floor, pedals and footrest. Provide space in front of and under the seat for longer legs to stretch. For a high seat, provide a footrest for the shortest legs.	Lower leg length.
Back-rest	Support (adjustable if possible) for the lower back is essential. If horizontal forward thrust is required, a high backrest should be considered.	Seat to lumbar curve.
Arm-rest	Provide a padded elbow rest where arm support is desirable.	Elbow height.

2.1.6. Work height

	The preferred height and angle of work depend on the task (elbow height for fine manipulation).	
Sitting	Match to the chosen sitting height. Design for the average seat/eye height position.	
Standing	Compromise between the reach and visual posture of the shortest and tallest user — it should be comfortable for both, if possible: *or* design for the average — taller users and add a platform for shorter users.	Waist height (height of highest obstruction to forward bending). Shoulder height. Eye height. Arm length.

2.1.7. Reach

Arm (one or two) — Design for the shortest arm and according to postural considerations and task requirement.
Guards should not cause trunk deflection.
In extreme forward reach there should be clearance for the head.

Shoulder – grip or finger tip.
Upper arm, forearm, hand, finger lengths.
Shoulder/elbow joint rotation.
Trunk bending/twisting.

Leg — Design the reach to the pedals for the shortest legs, with horizontal adjustment of the seat for longer legs.
Also include the horizontal adjustment of the pedal, if possible.

Arm reach zones — For placing work/controls of highest priority, highest frequency, longest duration, large force, high speed and accuracy: select the most comfortable reach zone for sitting or standing upright, facing forward, with the forearm below the heart and not greater than 45° to the side, and the elbow at the midpoint of the range or slightly bent.

Sitting/standing.

For low priority, low frequency, short duration activities select the most comfortable reach zone when at the limits of reach — the trunk bent and/or twisted.

Trunk bending/twisting.

2.1.8. Visual workspace

Eye position:
  Standing — Set the eye position for tallest, shortest and average user according to the body position chosen above.

Eye height, standing.

  Sitting — Allow for the forward adjustment of the seat.

Eye height, sitting.

  Obstructions — Check for obstructions to the line of vision between the object and the eye for a range of users.

Viewing posture:
  Zones of vision — For work and displays of high priority, frequency, long duration, high speed and accuracy, etc., select the most relaxed viewing position when the head is upright, facing forward and slightly inclined.

Cones (angles) of vision.

The normal line of sight should be 10° below horizontal for standing, 15° for sitting. This zone is best for attention, scanning, ability to see detail, colour (foveal vision, i.e., centre of eye used), and distance viewing.

17

	Medium priority visual zones should involve small eye/head rotation suitable for occasional reference.	Eye rotation.
	For low priority, low frequency, short duration viewing, etc., low priority visual zones involving head and/or trunk rotation/elevation may be used.	Head/trunk rotation.
Viewing distance	This must be appropriate for the size of the object and the illumination, etc.	Near point.
	It must not be closer than the furthest near point (recedes with age) of the user range.	Accommodation.
	Use optical aids where appropriate.	
Object:		
Size	The size must be appropriate for the viewing distance and conditions.	Acuity (angle subtended at eye — ability to see detail).
Contrast	It must be discriminable against the background in the poorest conditions by colour, luminance (brightness, contrast), shadow, shape, texture, or reflectance.	
Movement	This may be directional or vibrational, and leads to a drop in acuity. This can minimize interference with vision.	Speed of movement. Direction of movement: better towards the viewer than across the field of vision.
Visual defects	Allow ' .. ʋolour deficiencies 'ᴛ ...ɪy red) in designing displays, etc. Allow for reduced accommodation (hardening of the eye lens) with age. Allow for spectacles (especially bifocals).	

2.1.9. Illumination

General *Localized* *In-built*	Provide adequate illumination according to the requirements of the task (priority, duration, safety, etc.).	Illumination.
Acuity	The ability of the eye to detect detail increases with illumination.	
Contrast	The ability to discriminate between an object and its background is increased by differential reflection, not just by increased illumination.	
Direct glare	Avoid by altering the position of the lamp relative to the eye (the source should not be close to the line of sight) *or* by increasing the	Glare indices recommended in CIBS, 1984

size of the source *or* by choosing
diffused lighting *or* using screens.

Colour

The colour spectrum of the lamp
must be appropriate for the
colour requirements of the task
and the colours of the
components.

2.2. Body-size variations

2.2.1. General

Design for a *range* of users, not just the average (e.g., designing for
average reach means that the half of the user population with shorter
arms cannot reach).
Use the data available as a basis for judgement and first
approximation.
Confirm design details with adjustable mock-ups and representative
users where possible.

2.2.2. Variation

General

Body size varies with:
Body type — endomorph (obese), mesomorph (muscular), ectomorph
(thin);
Age — child, youth, adult, elderly;
Sex — male or female;
Nationality — e.g., British, Swedish;
Ethnic origin — e.g., European, Oriental;
Occupation/social group — e.g., general civilian, military, industrial,
clerical, etc.
Other factors — e.g., diet, deformities, disabilities.

Percentiles

It is uneconomic and impractical to design for extremes (large or
small).
It is common to design so that 90% (or 95%) of the proposed user
population can be accommodated, i.e., the smallest and largest 5%
(or 2.5%) are excluded. The smallest acceptable size is then the 5th
(or 2.5th) percentile and the largest acceptable size the 95th (or
97.5th) percentile.

Correlations

For crude purposes the lengths of body segments are generally taken
to be proportional to height and the segment sizes proportional to
body weight. In practice there is variation in body segment
proportions. This may be allowed for in design by considering, e.g., the
imaginary largest person with the shortest arms.

2.2.3. Body links

The main dimensions required are listed in the design decisions chart
p. 20. Others may be required, e.g., hand, for designing tools, handles,
etc.

For practical purposes the body can be approximated to a set of links
and joints. Muscles act across the joints and exert torques to maintain
posture, move the links and exert forces. Limitations of this approach,
e.g., a non-constant centre of rotation or a flexible spine can be
allowed for in practical design situations.

19

Figure 4. The main body links for consideration in ergonomic design.

Links	Joints
Head Shoulder Upper arms Forearms Hands Trunk Pelvis Thighs Lower legs Feet	Neck Shoulders Elbows Wrists Spine (base) Hips Knees Ankles

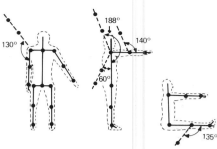

Typical joint rotation limits are shown (some variation between users).
(See Van Cott & Kinkade, 1972; and NIOSH, 1981.)

Postural comfort   Greatest in the resting position or with joints at the midpoint of the range

Postural discomfort   At extremes of joint rotation.
When limbs are furthest away from the trunk (especially above the head).
(Consider in terms of moments about joints and in terms of the muscles providing the resisting force.)
Static work, especially if the posture is uncomfortable or a change of position is not possible or a large force of long duration is exerted.

2.2.4. Limitations of data

General   Body-size data cannot be used alone without consideration of the nature of the activities being carried out — frequency, duration, postural comfort, rest pauses, etc (see the *Ergonomics check chart* p. 6).

Availability   Data are often unavailable for particular user populations, e.g., various occupational, social or ethnic groups.
Data from similar groups can be used as a basis for judgement but caution is needed and trials are advisable.
Some data are difficult to obtain without a literature search or may be unpublished or confidential in-house work.

Origins   Caution is needed in using design recommendations or data unless their origins are thoroughly explained — they may not be for a compatible situation. Use a variety of sources if in doubt.
Often single values are recommended without tolerance limits.
The surveys may have been carried out on too small a sample.
Much data have been obtained for military (particularly US) populations from which the smaller and obese will have been excluded. Care is needed in applying such data to general populations.

Measurements   For standardization, measurements are frequently of dimensions of nude subjects in an upright posture.
Data are mostly of static dimensions rather than dynamic (reach, etc.) measurements.
Data in various surveys may not be directly comparable, e.g., different dimensions, reference points, origins are used.
Allowances are needed for task requirements, slumped posture, dynamic reach, postural comfort and change of posture, clothing, etc.

High accuracy is not possible owing to the variability of body sizes, arbitrariness of percentile cut-off points, variation of height during the day due to spinal compression, slump causing up to 50 mm change in eye height, variation in the toleration of discomfort, the need to compromise when making design decisions, etc.

Application

Some translation of data is needed in order to apply it on the drawing board.

2.2.5. Conclusions

Design for the appropriate population.

Use data, if available, or make judgements from data for similar groups.

Carry out trials with representative users if possible.
See the data references in the *Bibliography*.

2.3. Suggested methods of workspace design

2.3.1. Introduction

This procedure, together with *Design decisions and principles* (p. 14), is offered to assist in setting out the workspace on the drawing board.

A simple approach from first principles is presented, which may be used for applying data obtained from references, surveys, trials, etc.

A direct check method using overlays is also presented.

The aim should be, within the limitations described, to allow a comfortable and efficient working posture and method for the proposed range of users.

The use of data should at least produce a good first approximation which may be confirmed by trials.

2.3.2. Design procedure

Given ranges of body lengths and sizes, the limits of rotation about joints and design principles, workspace limits (clearance, reach, visibility, etc.) can be drawn out.

Use overlays and references for dimensions.
Use the following reference points for defining the workspace for large, small and average users:
Floor.
Seat (intersection of lines of seat and seat back).
Eye.
Shoulder (centre of rotation for reach).

Figure 5. Flow chart of design procedure.

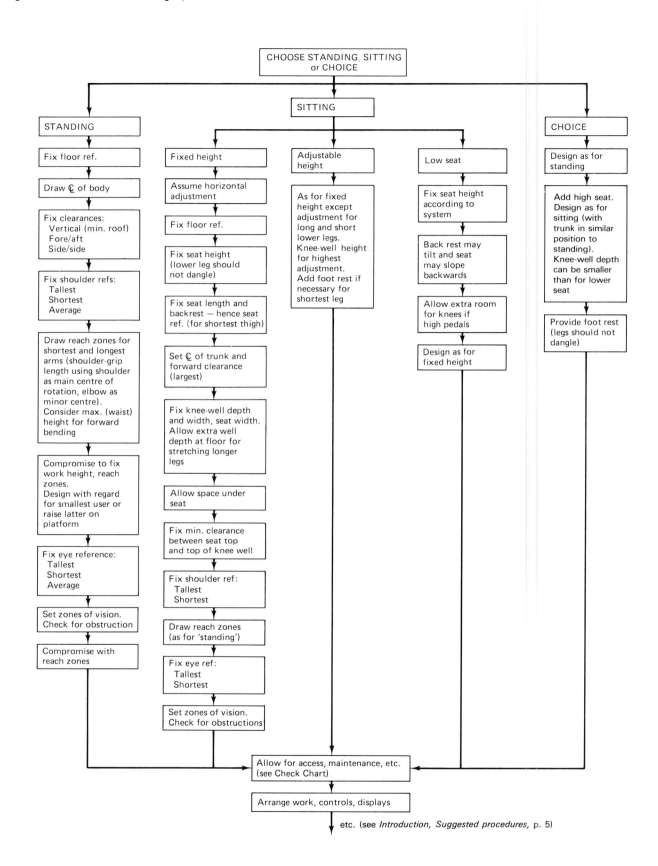

WORKSPACE

CHOOSE STANDING, SITTING or CHOICE

SITTING

STANDING

Fix floor ref.

Draw ₵ of body

Fix clearances:
Vertical (min. roof)
Fore/aft
Side/side

Fix shoulder refs:
Tallest
Shortest
Average

Draw reach zones for shortest and longest arms (shoulder-grip length using shoulder as main centre of rotation, elbow as minor centre). Consider max. (waist) height for forward bending

Compromise to fix work height, reach zones. Design with regard for smallest user or raise latter on platform

Fix eye reference:
Tallest
Shortest
Average

Set zones of vision. Check for obstruction

Compromise with reach zones

Fixed height

Assume horizontal adjustment

Fix floor ref.

Fix seat height (lower leg should not dangle)

Fix seat length and backrest — hence seat ref. (for shortest thigh)

Set ₵ of trunk and forward clearance (largest)

Fix knee-well depth and width, seat width. Allow extra well depth at floor for stretching longer legs

Allow space under seat

Fix min. clearance between seat top and top of knee well

Fix shoulder ref:
Tallest
Shortest

Draw reach zones (as for 'standing')

Fix eye ref:
Tallest
Shortest

Set zones of vision. Check for obstructions

Adjustable height

As for fixed height except adjustment for long and short lower legs. Knee-well height for highest adjustment. Add foot rest if necessary for shortest leg

Low seat

Fix seat height according to system

Back rest may tilt and seat may slope backwards

Allow extra room for knees if high pedals

Design as for fixed height

CHOICE

Design as for standing

Add high seat. Design as for sitting (with trunk in similar position to standing). Knee-well depth can be smaller than for lower seat

Provide foot rest (legs should not dangle)

Allow for access, maintenance, etc. (see Check Chart)

Arrange work, controls, displays

etc. (see *Introduction, Suggested procedures,* p. 5)

22

2.3.3. Direct check methods (Overlays)

General

The design principles and procedures, with suitable body-size data, can be used for predictive design from first principles.

For quick and direct checks or approximations the workspace drawings may be used indirectly, as transparent overlays. They can also be put under tracing paper as a guide during layout.

These drawings are based on the design principles and procedures and generalized data for UK adults. Judgement has been exercised in their construction and, for reasons already stated, a high degree of accuracy is not possible. However, for practical design situations, where compromises are inevitable, they present a useful first approximation.

The drawing can easily be modified by designers for particular situations or user populations and, by using the grid as a guide, can easily be reproduced to any scale.

Each drawing consists of a plan, side and rear sectional elevation set out on a 200 mm grid using floor, seat, eye and shoulder reference points (see *Design procedure*). High, medium and low priority reach and vision zones are drawn according to the *Design decisions and principles* (p. 17).

Reach and clearance

Reach zones are drawn for one arm (for two arms reduce the reach to the side).

Reach is drawn to the centre of the grip (for finger operation extension is possible).

Reach and clearance zones are presented for:

Standing (fixed floor):
(a) General UK population: small female (2·5 percentile) — large male (97·5 percentile).
(b) Larger UK population: small male (2·5 %ile) — large male (97·5 %ile), or average female — large female.

Sitting: For both population groups as for standing. For fixed, adjustable or high work chair.

Alternative reach zones and clearances may be drawn in proportion to arm length, body size, etc.

Vision

The zones of vision can be used for sitting or standing although the normal (relaxed) line of sight is 10° below horizontal for standing and 15° for sitting.

Use visual overlays in conjunction with reach overlays using eye reference point and check for compromises, obstructions, etc.

Preparation of overlays

Prepare a grid of appropriate size for the scale of drawing:

Scale	Grid size (mm)
1/2	100
1/4	50
1/5	40
1/10	20

Copy the drawings provided using the grid as a guide or produce modified versions for other user populations;
or use reduction copying or other methods of preparation.

Reference points

Reference Points	Eye	Floor	Seat	Shoulder
General	ERP	FRP	SRP	SHRP
Small (2.5%) female	E2.5F	F2.5F	S2.5F	SH2.5F
Small (2.5%) male	E2.5M	F2.5M	S2.5M	SH2.5M
Large (97.5%) male	E97.5M	F97.5M	S97.5M	SH97.5M

Some reference points are not shown on the drawings but may have been used in their construction.

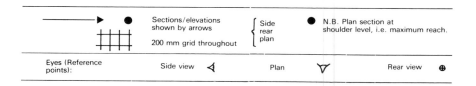

Table 4. Zones of reach and vision according to frequency of use.

		Reach zone	Visual zone
H	High	For locating work and controls of highest priority, highest frequency and duration of operation, large force *or* high speed *or* high accuracy. Most comfortable reach zone, sitting or standing upright facing forward forearm below heart and > 45° to side, elbow at mid-point range or slightly bent.	For locating work and displays of highest priority, frequency, duration, etc. Most relaxed viewing posture: head upright or slightly inclined, facing forward. Best zone for scanning, attention, acuity, colour vision and distance viewing.
M	Medium	For locating work and controls of medium priority and frequency, duration, etc. Sitting/standing uprights. Small eye/head rotation. Arm at limit of reach to front and sides. Forearm allowed above shoulder.	For locating work and displays of medium priority, duration, etc. Zone viewed by small eye/head rotation.
L	Low	For locating work and controls of low priority, low frequency, short duration, low force, speed and accuracy. Maximum reach by bending and/or rotating back.	For work and displays of low priority, frequency, duration, etc. Zone viewed by rotation/elevation head and trunk rotation.

W O R K S P A C E

24

Figure 6. Reach and vision zones.

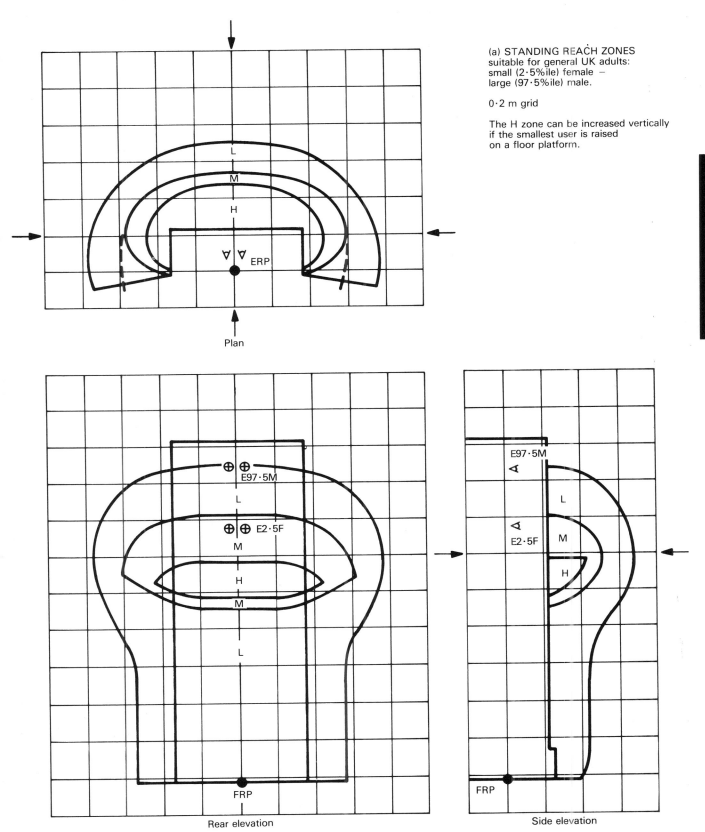

(a) STANDING REACH ZONES
suitable for general UK adults:
small (2·5%ile) female —
large (97·5%ile) male.

0·2 m grid

The H zone can be increased vertically
if the smallest user is raised
on a floor platform.

Plan

Rear elevation

Side elevation

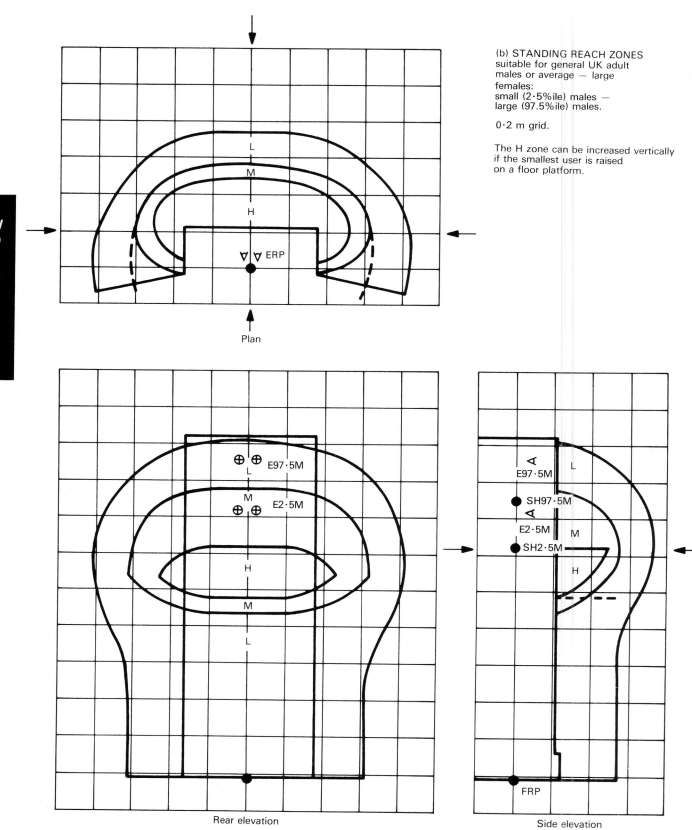

(b) STANDING REACH ZONES
suitable for general UK adult
males or average — large
females:
small (2·5%ile) males —
large (97.5%ile) males.

0·2 m grid.

The H zone can be increased vertically
if the smallest user is raised
on a floor platform.

Plan

Rear elevation

Side elevation

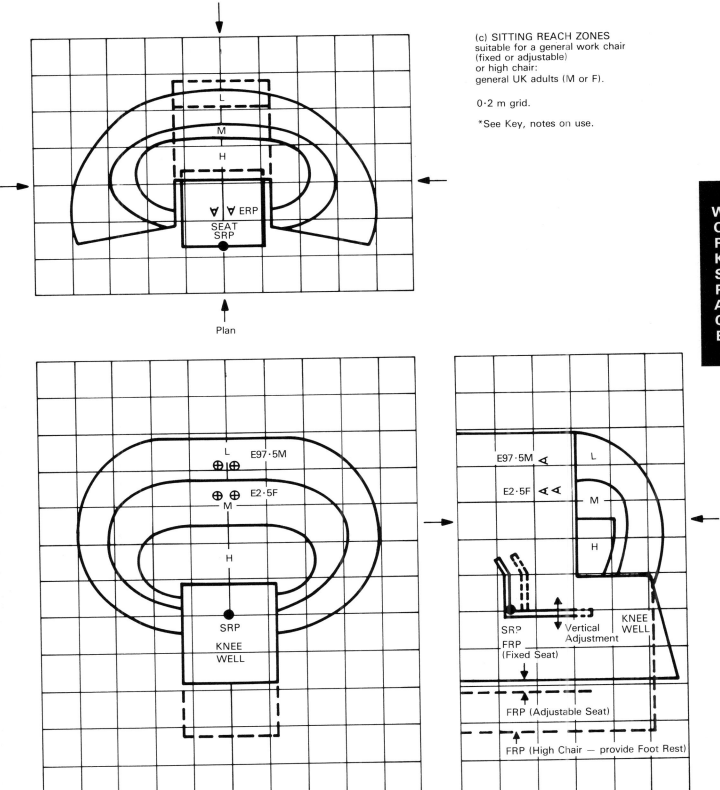

(c) SITTING REACH ZONES
suitable for a general work chair
(fixed or adjustable)
or high chair:
general UK adults (M or F).

0·2 m grid.

*See Key, notes on use.

Plan

Rear elevation

Side elevation

L

M

H

ERP

SEAT
SRP

E97·5M

E2·5F

M

H

SRP

KNEE
WELL

E97·5M

E2·5F

L

M

H

KNEE
WELL

Vertical
Adjustment

SRP

FRP
(Fixed Seat)

FRP (Adjustable Seat)

FRP (High Chair — provide Foot Rest)

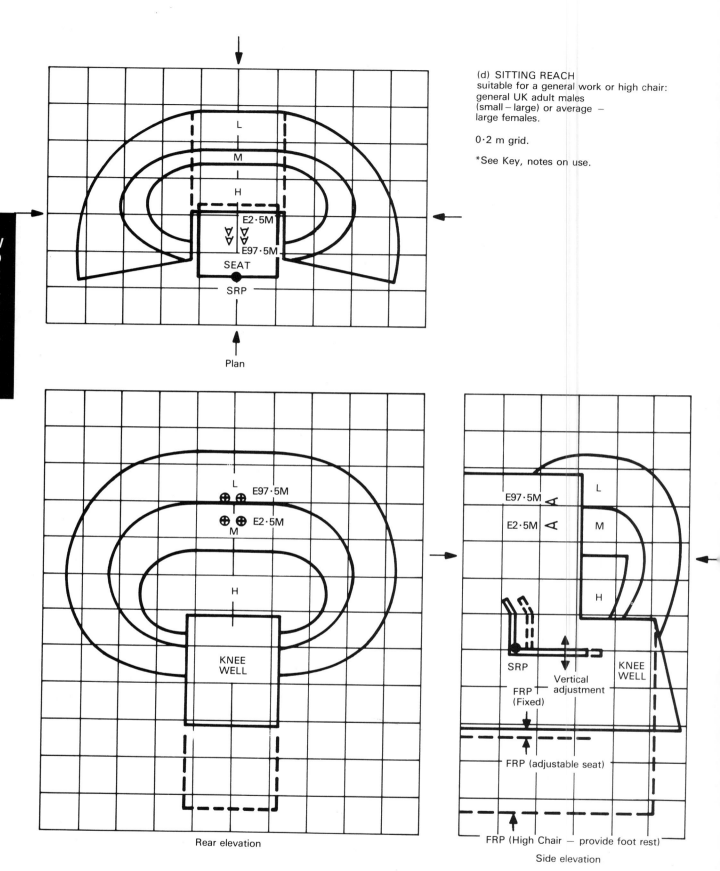

(d) SITTING REACH
suitable for a general work or high chair:
general UK adult males
(small – large) or average –
large females.

0·2 m grid.

*See Key, notes on use.

Plan

Rear elevation

Side elevation

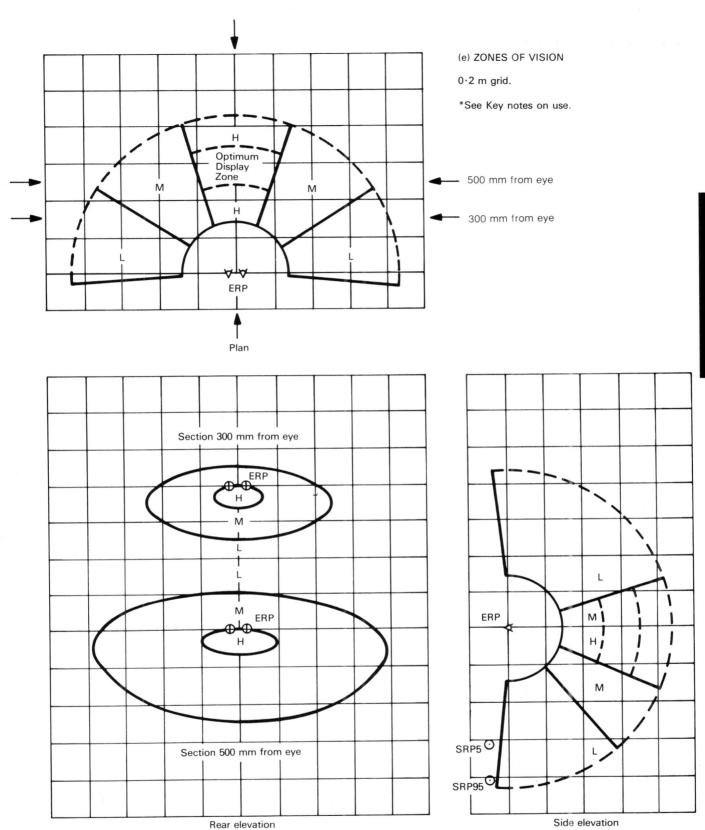

(e) ZONES OF VISION

0·2 m grid.

*See Key notes on use.

← 500 mm from eye

← 300 mm from eye

Optimum
Display
Zone

H

M

M

H

L

L

ERP

Plan

Section 300 mm from eye

ERP

H

M

L

L

M

ERP

H

Section 500 mm from eye

Rear elevation

ERP

L

M

H

M

L

SRP5

SRP95

Side elevation

2.4. Clearance, access, size and safety distance details

2.4.1. Introduction

The following is intended as useful information to be used with the overlays.

These tabulated data provide recommended dimensions. They are not exhaustive of all possibilities but deal with general cases.

The dimensions will need to be tested to see how adequate they are in practice (see pp. 38 – 39).

Reach dimensions all assume a grip with a full fist, not fingertip dimensions.

If the worker is to sit or stand, use knee and foot clearances from the sitting section with heights increased to set the work surface at standing height. Provide a footrest at floor height as specified in the "seated worker" section.

If the work height is greater than 50 mm from the recommended and the equipment cannot be changed, provide a false floor.

2.4.2. Clearance

Figure 7. Clearance and access dimensions for a standing worker.

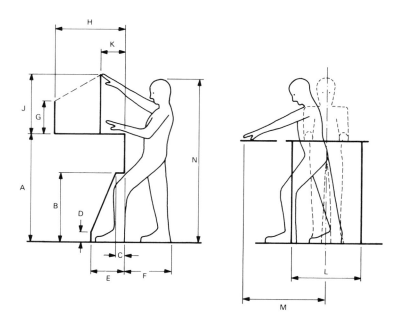

		%ile men (in mm)			%ile women (in mm)			
Code	Dimension	5	50	95	5	50	95	Comments
A	Work surface height (elbow)	970	1070	1190	905	995	1065	
B	Knee clearance height			560				Minimum required clearance
C	Knee clearance depth			125				
D	Toe clearance height			100				
E	Toe clearance depth			250				
F	Back clearance			915				
G	Max. reach access height	380			380			
H	Max. reach access distance	915			890			
J	Upright reach access height	685			635			
K	Upright reach access distance	455			405			
L	Crouch space for side pick-up			1145				
M	Extent of max. side reach[a]	1145						
N	Standing workers height	1600	1730	1880	1505	1605	1695	

[a]For a twisted trunk, M will be less than stated.

Figure 8. Clearance and access dimensions for a seated worker.

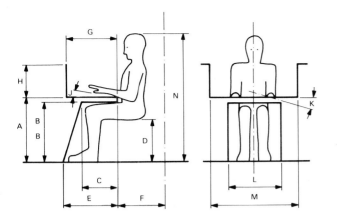

Code	Dimensions	% ile men (in mm)			% ile women (in mm)			Comments
		5	50	95	5	50	95	
A	Work surface height	660	710	760	635	685	735	
B	Knee clearance height (cross-legged)			750			725	Minimum required clearance
B'	Knee clearance height (un-crossed)			625			600	Minimum required clearance
C	Knee clearance depth			350			350	
D	Seat height (horizontal seat)	447	483	523	424	460	495	Use 5th % ile if only using min. B
E	Foot clearance depth			650			650	
F	Clearance for getting up			635			635	
G	Grasp objects depth	610			610			Assumes slight leaning
H	Grasp objects height	380			380			Assumes slight leaning
J	Keyboard or switch panel angle		15°			15°		
K	Keyboard angle for one-handed operation		20°			20°		
L	Knee-well depth			650			650	
M	Distance apart of side panels for max. reach to grasp to height H	1650			1500			
N	Max. head height			1450				

2.4.3. Access

Table 5. Access clearance and size details.

		Height (mm)	Width (mm)	
WORKSTATION	See *Overlays* for seated and standing workspace clearances			
ADDITIONS TO DIMENSIONS	The following are minimum recommended dimensions. Extra allowances should be made for equipment, tools, removing components etc.			
GANGWAYS, AISLES	Minimum (moving sideways) Feeder aisles 2 people passing (one sideways) 2 people passing Catwalks	1000 (stoop) 2000 (walk)	330 510-765 765-915 1200-1375 Base 370 Top 635	
	Crawling	800	515	
	Prone	440	515	
LADDERS, STAIRS	Use ladder if rise > 50° or stairs impracticable			
	Rise 75-90°. Provide guard rail at top. Ladder with rungs 32-38 mm dia. Rise 50-75°. Ladder with treads of depth 75-150 mm		500 min	
	Rise 50°. Use stairs (opt. rise 30-35°) Rise <15°. Ramp may be used	Rise 125-200 Going depth 240-265		
	Provide handrail 850-900 mm above stairs		As for aisles	
OPENINGS, HOLES	Empty hand, flat Hand plus screwdriver Fist, clenched Inserting box with hands Thumb plus 2 fingers Hole for reaching to 150 mm (hands clasped) Hole for reaching to 645 mm Full arm reach	60 100 110 50 105 105 >100	105 100 110 Box size + 45 50 115 460 600	
HANDLES	Provide handles, especially for components weighing over 4·5 kg	CLEARANCE, C MIN 50 OPT 65 (GLOVED) RAD, R 3 mm (< 7 Kg) — 10 mm (> 9 Kg) SEPARATION, S MIN 50 mm WIDTH, W ONE HAND 110 (bare) — 120 (gloved) 2 HANDS 220-240		

WORKSPACE

2.4.4. Manual handling of loads

Factors affecting ability to handle loads

Weight of load.
Dimensions.
Horizontal distance of the load from the lifter.
Distance the load is moved from its origin to its destination.
Height the load is lifted vertically:
from its origin to its destination;
height of the origin from the floor.
1- or 2-person lift.
Mechanical aids.

Weight

1 person:
Maximum for males   =   20 kg.
Maximum for females   =   14 kg.
2 people:
Up to 40 kg, less for women. Label with weight and/or that load needs 2 people. If lifted over 1500 mm and weighing over 16 kg (for men), use a mechanical lift.
Mechanical lifts must be used for loads and heights greater than specified, and warning labels and lifting eyes or other points must be provided.
Note that usable strength is related to many factors, including age, posture, fitness, training and experience, duration of effort and frequency of lift.
In general, reduce all loads by 1/3 for people over 40.
Lifting tasks can be categorized into 3 classes:
1. Those above the maximum permissible limit (M.P.L.). These are unacceptable and require engineering solutions.
2. Those between the M.P.L. and the action limit (A.L.). These are unacceptable without some form of engineering modification or other changes, e.g., worker selection and training.
    Note: if selection is necessary, then training in handling is also necessary.
3. Those below the A.L., which are within the capabilities of 99% of men and 75% of women adults (US figures from NIOSH, 1981).
    Note: make appropriate adjustments for other populations in proportion to ratios of mean strengths.
Figure 9 shows the three zones for infrequent lifting from the floor to knuckle height.

Figure 9. Maximum weight vs. horizontal location for infrequent lifts from floor to knuckle height.

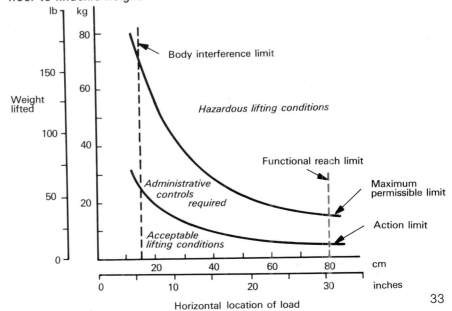

If weight, vertical distance and frequency of the lift are known, maximum *acceptable* weights of lift, for two widths of load and for two heights of lift, are shown in figure 10. The graphs assume a load with good handles, able to be reached and held close to the body and not carried horizontally. They are also for people up to 40 years; reduce the loads by 1/3 for those between 40 and 60.

Figure 10. Maximum acceptable weight of lift for 90% of American adult population showing effect of height of lift, frequency of lift, width of object, male and female differences (Snook, 1970).

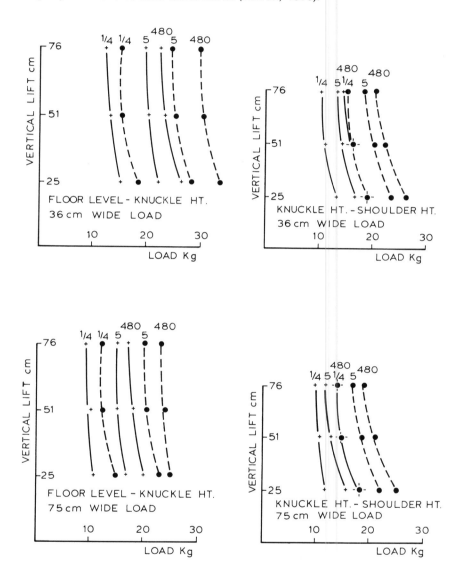

Key: ● =   Male 90%ile
       + =   Female 90%ile
¼, 5, 480 =   Interval between lift in mins

When loads are manually handled, avoid designs which would require the lifter's trunk to rotate to reach or place the load. Very high and dangerous back loads can be created where lifts are not symmetrical in front of the body.

2.4.5. Safety distances

General

These correspond to a reach or body dimension plus a safety allowance, and are measured from points which are accessible for operating, maintaining and inspection.

The aim is to maintain hazard points (squeezing, shearing, cutting, etc.) at a safe distance from the operator.

The following dimensions are extracted from DIN 31001 part 1. These are currently being investigated for suitability for the UK and possible adoption by BS. (dimensions are for adults and in mm).

Some information on openings in guards is provided to BS 5304 (*Safeguarding of machinery*) figure 6, and also BS 3042 (*Standard test fingers and probes*)

Figure 11. Safety distances for whole-body reach.

Reaching up
With the body upright and standing at full height, the safety distance when reaching up is 2500 mm.

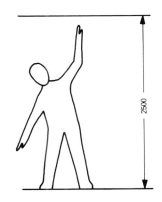

Reaching down, reaching over
When reaching down over an edge, e.g, on machine frames or safety features, the safety distance is found from:
A — Distance of hazard point from floor
B — Height of edge of safety feature
C — Horizontal distance of edge of hazard point

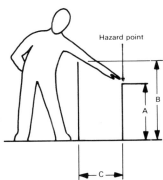

Distance of hazard point from floor A	Height of edge of safety feature B[a] (in mm)							
	2400	2200	2000	1800	1600	1400	1200	1000
	Horizontal distance C from hazard point							
2400	—	100	100	100	100	100	100	100
2200	—	250	350	400	500	500	600	600
2000	—	—	350	500	600	700	900	1100
1800	—	—	—	600	900	900	1000	1100
1600	—	—	—	500	900	900	1000	1300
1400	—	—	—	100	800	900	1000	1300
1200	—	—	—	—	500	900	1000	1400
1000	—	—	—	—	300	900	1000	1400
800	—	—	—	—	—	600	900	1300
600	—	—	—	—	—	—	500	1200
400	—	—	—	—	—	—	300	1200
200	—	—	—	—	—	—	200	1100

[a] Values for edge B under 100 mm have not been included because the reach does not increase any further and in addition there is the risk of falling into the hazard area.

Reaching round

This covers the safety distance of freely articulating body parts around edges in any position, for adults and children.
The radius of movement about a fixed edge is determined by the reach of given body parts. The safety distances assigned below must be respected as minima if the body part concerned is not to be allowed to reach a hazard point. Of special importance is the hazard area which can be reached when these body parts are introduced through slots.
When applying safety distances it is to be assumed that the basic joint component of the relevant body part is in fixed contact with the edge. The safety distances apply only if it is ensured that further advance or penetration of the body part towards the hazard point is excluded.

Figure 12. Safety distances for reach of body parts.

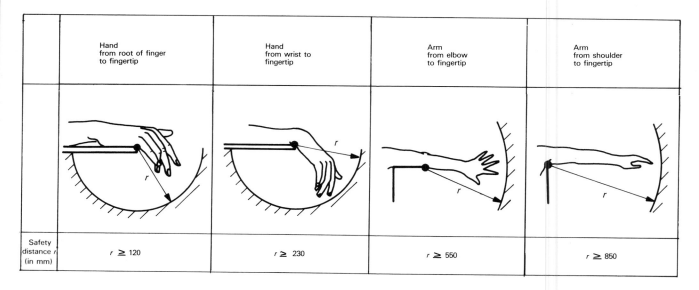

	Hand from root of finger to fingertip	Hand from wrist to fingertip	Arm from elbow to fingertip	Arm from shoulder to fingertip
Safety distance r (in mm)	$r \geq 120$	$r \geq 230$	$r \geq 550$	$r \geq 850$

Figure 13. Safety dimensions for elongated apertures with parallel sides.

	Finger-tip	Finger	Hand to ball of thumb	Arm
Aperture rectangle or gap a (in mm)	$> 4 \leq 8$	$> 8 \leq 20$	$> 20 \leq 30$	$> 30 \leq 135$[a]
Safety distance to hazard point b (in mm)	≥ 15	≥ 120	≥ 200	≥ 850

[a] With measurements exceeding the stated aperture it is possible for the body to stoop in, so that the safety distances in accordance with Section 2.4.3, p. 32 are to be taken into account.

Figure 14. Safety dimensions for square or circular apertures.

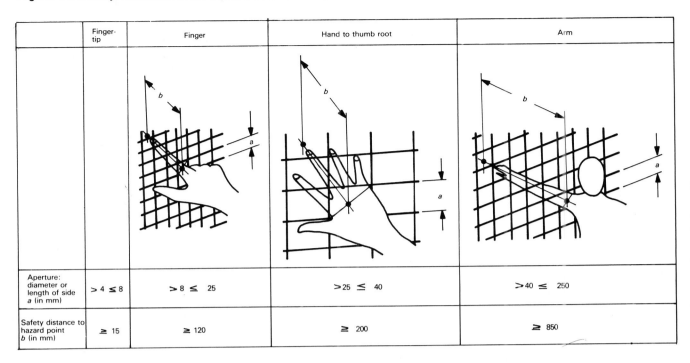

	Finger-tip	Finger	Hand to thumb root	Arm
Aperture: diameter or length of side *a* (in mm)	> 4 ≤ 8	> 8 ≤ 25	> 25 ≤ 40	> 40 ≤ 250
Safety distance to hazard point *b* (in mm)	≥ 15	≥ 120	≥ 200	≥ 850

Figure 15. Safety dimensions at squeeze points.

A squeeze point is not regarded as a hazard point for the indicated body parts if the safety distances are not less than shown below and if it is ensured that the next larger body part cannot be introduced:

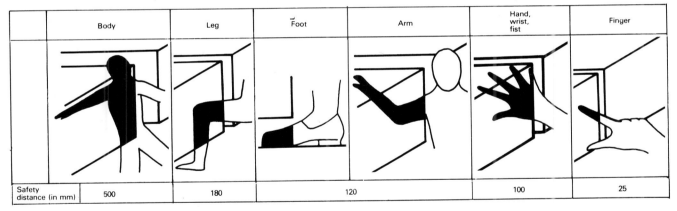

	Body	Leg	Foot	Arm	Hand, wrist, fist	Finger
Safety distance (in mm)	500	180	120		100	25

2.5. Fitting trials

2.5.1. General

The use of the following approach is recommended for confirmation of preliminary designs and first approximations (see *Limitations of data,* pp. 20 – 21).

Full trials are recommended or, if time is limited, abbreviated procedures are valuable.

List all user actions and carry out trials for all main actions affecting dimensions and layout.

Users should be representative in terms of size ranges, training, etc. Evaluations are more satisfactory when two or more alternatives are compared. Where one proposed design is tried, subjects' performances and judgements must be compared with an assumed normal unless a fairly simple design decision is being tested. (The design is acceptable if the subjects do better or no worse than the assumed normal.)

2.5.2. Simulator

May be simple (e.g., cardboard) for quick checks of simple problems, or more complex (slotted angles, softboard, etc.) for more important problems or detailed evaluations.

Each significant dimension should be adjustable without altering other significant dimensions.

Quick alteration is essential (so that memory can be used in comparison).

Set up the simulator according to a first approximation based on design principles, check charts, etc.

2.5.3. Designer as subject

This is an opportunity for the designer to systematically decide on standards of convenience and comfort for each operator action.

The designer reproduces the operator's actions and adjusts each significant dimension in turn to establish a range of settings compatible with the appropriate range of body sizes and assessments of convenience and comfort.

The importance of each dimension and maximum/minimum limiting points are established.

2.5.4. Abbreviated method

If full trials are not possible estimate limiting settings for extreme sizes:

$$\text{Extreme subject's setting} = \text{designer's setting} \times \frac{\text{extreme subject's height}}{\text{designer's height}}$$

Omit all but the most critical maxima/minima.

2.5.5. Full trials
Subjects

Try out with the designer as the subject, and then with a range of subjects.

Ensure that the subjects are representative in body size (see *Body-size variations,* p. 19).

Arbitrarily cut off the extremes (e.g., 5th and 95th percentiles; see *Body-size variations,* p. 19).

Pick fairly tall and fairly short subjects. Use tall fat and short fat subjects if possible, as they are less adaptable than thin people — if there is no discomfort for fat people then there will not be for thin either.

Subjects should be of an appropriate age, background, and skill.

Allow for attitude, practice, tiredness, and individual differences.

Testing

Determine the range of each of the dimensions to be tested which is acceptable to each subject.
Set all dimensions to an average position.
The subject carries out one of the operator actions. The dimension to be tested is adjusted with the others constant.
Adjustment begins with the dimension at an initial setting much below the acceptable minimum.
Adjustment is increased in steps (e.g., 25 mm) until it is above the acceptable maximum, and then reduced again to below the acceptable minimum.
The subject compares the comfort of each setting with the previous setting or each setting with an estimate of what is an intolerable degree of discomfort or inconvenience (e.g., "is this better" or "is this tolerable").
It is thus possible to obtain minimum and maximum tolerable and optimum settings for increasing and decreasing adjustments.
Tolerance ranges are obtained for each dimension for each subject and plotted.
The ranges are found at settings not outside the tolerance ranges of any subject.

Figure 16. The tolerance range of dimensions.

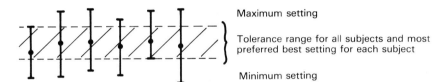

Maximum setting

Tolerance range for all subjects and most preferred best setting for each subject

Minimum setting

If there is no overlap, redesign or make adjustable.
If there are incompatible combinations adjust all dimensions within the final range or find combinations of settings involving the smallest departure from the intended degree of comfort and convenience.

3. Environmental Design

ENVIRONMENT

3.1. Introduction

3.1.1. General arrangements

The ergonomic criteria for a good environment are those which will aid people in achieving their objectives whilst retaining effort, stress and errors within tolerable limits. The environment should be designed to help people, rather than just to remove its more objectionable or unacceptable features.

This section covers three of the six environmental factors:
Thermal;
Visual;
Auditory.

Figure 17. Major environmental factors in workspace design.

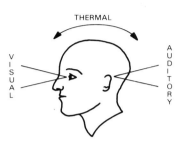

The three factors not covered are:
Vibrational;
Chemical;
Radiation.

Each environmental factor will be considered in isolation. The components of each factor combine to cause the sensation and responses to the factor, whether or not it is safe, acceptable, etc. At the end of each section texts are recommended to provide more information, particularly concerning the complex interactions between factors.

3.2. The auditory environment

3.2.1. Basic principles

Noise is unwanted sound. Legally the average level of noise should not exceed 90 dB during the length of a working day to protect 90% of the exposed population from suffering deafness. But noise also hinders performance, hence attention must be paid to other facets of the noise and to the requirements of the job.

3.2.2. The effects of a poor auditory environment

Negligent design of auditory environments can:
Inhibit speech communication;
Mask warning signals;
Reduce mental performance;
Induce nausea and headaches;
Induce tinnitus (ringing in the ears);
Temporarily impair hearing;
Cause temporary deafness;
Cause permanent deafness.

3.2.3. The main factors in the auditory environment

Intensity

Intensity is the sound level or loudness: the pressure of the sound waves.

The loudness is measured as the ratio of the sound pressure to that of the pressure for a just-audible sound. The ratio is logarithmic, to enable the enormous range of audibility to be expressed in convenient numbers.

Unit of intensity $= N\ m^{-2}$.
Unit of loudness (i.e., the human perception of intensity) $= dB(A)$.
Noise intensity for an 8 h exposure should not exceed 90 dB(A).
Very short exposures should not exceed 135 dB(A), except for impulse noise whose instantaneous level should never exceed 150 dB(A).

Speech Interference Levels (SILs) will give guidance on the noise levels which interfere with speech communication.

Two noises must have a difference in intensity of about 10 dB before they can be separated by the ear.
A change of 3 dB means doubling the physical effect of the noise; small changes in level are thus important.

Figure 18. Noise levels which barely permit reliable conversation.

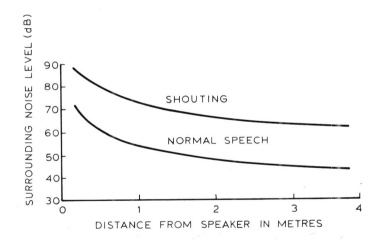

Frequency

Frequency, or pitch, is the rate of repetition of the cycles.
Human perception of frequency (in the audible range) varies with loudness.
In the normal range of industrial noise human hearing is more sensitive to the higher frequencies.
If high frequency noise is present, then shorter exposure times or lower intensities are required for equivalent exposure effects.

Unit of frequency $=$ Hertz (Hz) (1 Hz $=$ 1 cycle per second).
High frequencies mask lower frequencies.

Fluctuating frequency noise can be heard over a steady pitch.

Exposure time

Exposure time is the maximum time unprotected ears may be exposed to different intensities and frequencies of noise.

This example is from Swedish Standards (SEN 590111) at 1000 Hz.

Total exposure during one day	Maximum intensity (dB(A))
> 5 h	85
5 – 2 h	90
2 – 1 h	95
< 20 min	105
< 5 min	120

Figure 19. Maximum exposure time during a working day (from Swedish Standard SEN 590111).

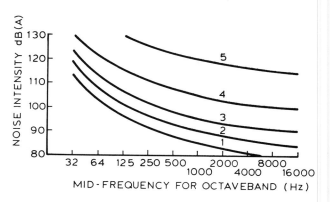

1. > 5 hours
2. 2 – 5 hours
3. 1 – 2 hours
4. < 20 mins
5. < 5 mins

Where the intensity cannot be controlled at source ear defenders and ear plugs can lengthen the permissible exposure period depending on the sound attenuating characteristics of the equipment, but a regular audiometric survey programme is desirable.
Ear defenders and ear plugs reduce *all* sound, including warning signals and speech.

3.2.4. Infrasound

Infrasound is very low frequency sound. Research has shown that at the lower end of the sound spectrum, 16 – 3.5 Hz, subjects have complained of the sensations of vertigo, nausea and headaches.

3.2.5. Ultrasound

Ultrasound is very high frequency sound. There is insufficient evidence to support the case that ultrasound induces sickness.

3.2.6. Legal requirements

The legal requirements are laid out in *Noise and the Worker,* by Her Majesty's Factory Inspectorate (1971).

3.2.7. Non-legal requirements

Just meeting the legal requirements is often misleading; they are only the maximum limits for minimizing deafness.
Noise within the legal limits can still have a very disturbing effect, especially on mental performance.
For a general appreciation of the influence of sound see Burns (1973).

3.3. The thermal environment

3.3.1. Basic principle

To provide an environment which imposes as small a load as possible on the body's own thermoregulatory system.
The heat exchanges between the body and its environment can be simply represented by the heat balance equation:

$$M \pm C_1 \pm C_2 \pm R - E = S$$

where M is the heat due to metabolism, including physical work effort; C_1, C_2 and R are the heat lost or gained by convection, conduction and radiation; E is the heat lost due to the evaporation of sweat; and S is the amount of heat lost or gained by the tissues of the body. If the body maintains thermal equilibrium, then $S = 0$.

3.3.2. The effects of a poor thermal environment

Negligent design of thermal environments can cause:
Reduced physical performance;
Irritability and distraction from the task, and reduced mental performance;
Discomfort from sweating or shivering;
Increased load on the heart;
Death.

3.3.3. The main factors in the thermal environment

Activity level

The activity level affects metabolism. Physical activity generates body heat, which the environment must compensate for.
High workloads require cooler environments.
Low workloads require warmer environments.

Activity level unit = kcal h^{-1} m^{-2} (heat equivalent per hour per square metre of body surface).

An example from Fanger (1972).

Activity	Metabolism (kcal h^{-1} m^{-2})
Draughtsman	60
Light machine work	100 – 120
Heavy machine work	200
Slag removal in a foundry	380

Clothing

If special clothing is worn as part of the job this will change the heat loss equation.
Remember that people's dress habits change seasonally *regardless* of the indoor environment.

Clothing unit = clo values or a verbal description, i.e., light, medium, winter, etc.

An example from Fanger (1972).

Clothing	Clo factor
Nude	0
Light summer clothes (male)	0·5
Heavy business suit	1·5
Polar weather suit	3 – 4

Ambient temperature

Ambient temperature (also known as air temperature or dry bulb temperature) is simply the temperature of the surrounding air.
Air temperature alone is *not* a sufficient measure of the suitability of an environment. Here are some examples of the order of temperatures for different types of job.
Ambient temperature is measured by a conventional mercury in glass thermometer (dry bulb).

An example from Bell (1974).

Activity	Temperature (°C)
Clerical work	20·0 – 19·5
General office work	19·5 – 18·3
Active workers in light industry	18·3 – 15·5
Heavy industry	15·5 – 12·8

Humidity

Humidity (or relative humidity) is the water content of air.
Humidity can vary over a wide range without much effect in normal working conditions.
Humidity is critical in a hot environment where it will restrict heat loss by evaporation.
Humidity is measured by using wet and dry bulb thermometers and hygrometric tables.

Humidity units = % water saturation of air.

An example from Bell (1974).
At 18·5°C for general office work humidity could range from 30 – 70% with little change in human comfort.

Air flow	Air flow (or air speed) is the velocity of air at the individual workplace. Air flow is important for cooling and for the sensation of fresh air. Air flow is measured by an anemometer.	Air flow unit $= $ m s^{-1}. An example from Bell (1974). A mean air flow of $0 \cdot 11 - 0 \cdot 15$ m s^{-1} would be judged comfortable. $0 \cdot 5$ m s^{-1} is judged uncomfortably draughty.
Radiant temperature	Radiant heat is the heat energy transferred *to or from* the body through radiation. In most cases it is the radiant temperature transmitted to the body which is of interest. Where the radiant temperature exceeds the ambient temperature by 10°C or more the sources should be shielded. Where the operator is given protective clothing to reduce the effect of radiant heat a new microclimate is created and the normal processes of heat loss are severely restricted. Hence this may increase discomfort and reduce work capacity due to the heat gain within the clothing. Radiant temperature is measured by a mercury in glass thermometer within a blackened copper ball, a 'globe thermometer'.	Radiant temperature unit $= $ °C. An acceptable radiant temperature range is 16° – 20°C. An unduly cold or warm surface, by accepting or emitting radiant heat, affects feelings of comfort. Note that increased air flow does not compensate for radiant heat exposure: shielding is necessary.

3.3.4. Techniques to evaluate the thermal environment

Thermal stress	The international standard scale (ISO 7243, 1982) to evaluate thermal stress is the wet bulb globe temperature, WBGT.
Thermal comfort	A widely accepted scale for thermal comfort in more moderate environments is Fanger's Thermal Comfort Index.
Cold environments	No standard reference exists.

3.3.5. Legal requirements

The legal requirements are set out in the Factories Act, 1961. The legal requirements are the minimum requirements and do not imply that the conditions are optimal.

E N V I R O N M E N T

3.4. The visual environment

3.4.1. Basic principle

The aim of designing visual environments is not to provide light but to allow people to recognize what they see. (NB The visual environment is the most complex of the three to design.)

3.4.2. The effects of a poor visual environment

Negligent design of visual environments can induce:
Visual discomfort and headaches;
Errors and inability to see detail;
Confusion, illusions and disorientation;
Epilepsy (where it is already present).

3.4.3. The main factors in the visual environment

Illuminance

Illuminance is the amount of light *falling* onto a surface.
The amount of illumination required to light adequately a task depends on the task.
Illuminance falls off as the square of the distance from the source.
Recommended levels can be found for almost all tasks in the CIBS code.
Illuminance is measured by a light meter at the work surface.

Illuminance unit = Lux (SI).

An example from the CIBS Code (1984).

Task	Illuminance (Lux)
Loading bays, storerooms	150 – 300
Packing work, mould preparation, general engineering	300 – 500
Office work, fine engineering, inspection and steel works	500 – 800
Drawing office, garage and tool room, watchmaking	> 800

Luminance

Luminance is defined as the amount of light emitted by a surface.
A luminance ratio of 10:3:1 between the task to the surrounding area to the general background has been found to be comfortable.
Excessive luminance causes glare.
Insufficient luminance reduces visibility.

Luminance unit = candela m^{-2} (SI).
See *Contrast* for formula.
Concentration is helped if the work area is the brightest part of the visual field.

Contrast

An object can be seen and its shape identified because of its contrast with its background.
Contrast can be improved by:
Changing the level of illumination;
Changing the reflectivity of certain parts of the task;
Using directional lighting to cast shadows.

There is no agreed measure of contrast. The most common method is

$$C = (L_1 - L_2)/L_1$$

where C is the contrast or luminance ratio; L_1 is the brighter of the two luminances; and L_2 is the lower of the two luminances.

48

Glare

Glare occurs when there are areas of high brightness in the visual field.

There are two main types of glare (both must be avoided):
Discomfort glare, i.e., glare which causes discomfort only;
Disability glare, which causes discomfort and a drop in visual performance by reducing the ability to see detail.

Glare from a single source is measured and expressed as a glare constant (see Hopkinson & Collins).

This is then converted to a Glare Index.

Where there is more than one glare source at a workplace, they can be summed to give the Glare Index.

An example from CIBS code (1984).
(a) Environments where no glare is permissible:
Glare Index Limit = 10.
(b) Environments where glare must be kept to a minimum:
Glare Index Limit = 13.
(c) Environments where different degrees of glare are permitted depending on the sensitivity of people, the time spent in a room and the attention demanded by work:
Glare Index Limit = 16 − 28.

Flicker

Flicker arises from poor quality fluorescent fittings or rotating parts between a light source and the eye.

If it cannot be eliminated, arrange that the flicker is greater than the Critical Flicker Fusion Frequency (CFF) of people for the level of field luminance. The CFF is the frequency at which flicker becomes imperceptible. This threshold varies greatly between people but can be as high as 85 Hz, i.e., higher than mains frequency.

Also, the greater the luminance level the greater the human sensitivity to flicker.

Flicker can be noticed more easily at the edge of the field of vision. Distribution of lights across the three phases of the power supply, and the choice of phosphors in fluorescent lights, can eliminate flicker.

Colour

Artificial lighting has colour. Choosing the colour of lighting is important emotionally and with respect to colour.

Coloured objects look white under light of their own colour and black under light of a complementary colour, e.g., red objects look white in red light and black in green light.

1. Emotionally.

Verbal impressions associated with different levels and colours of fluorescent lighting in a conference room.

An example from Bodman (1967; cited in Hopkinson and Collins).

Average illumination (Lux)	Colour of light		
	Warm white	White	Daylight
700	Not un-pleasant	Dim	Cool
700 – 3000	Pleasant	Pleasant	Neutral
3000	Exces-sive, arti-ficial	Pleasant, lively	Pleasant

2. With respect to performance. Where colour is important in the task to indicate danger or the quality of goods (i.e., inspection), select lighting which increases the contrast of the colour to be recognized against the background.

The visual state of the operator

If complaints occur about the state of the visual environment or about visual performance, consider the possibility of examining the visual state of the operator.

3.4.4. Legal requirements

The legal requirements are set out in *Lighting in Offices, Shops and Railway Premises,* (London: HMSO, 1978).
Note that the legal requirements are lower than the IES recommendations. Where possible follow the IES Code of Practice.
The way the factors which make up the visual environment interact is complicated and requires the advice of a lighting engineer.

4. Control Design

C
O
N
T
R
O
L

4.1. Design criteria

Figure 20. Flow chart of criteria for control design.

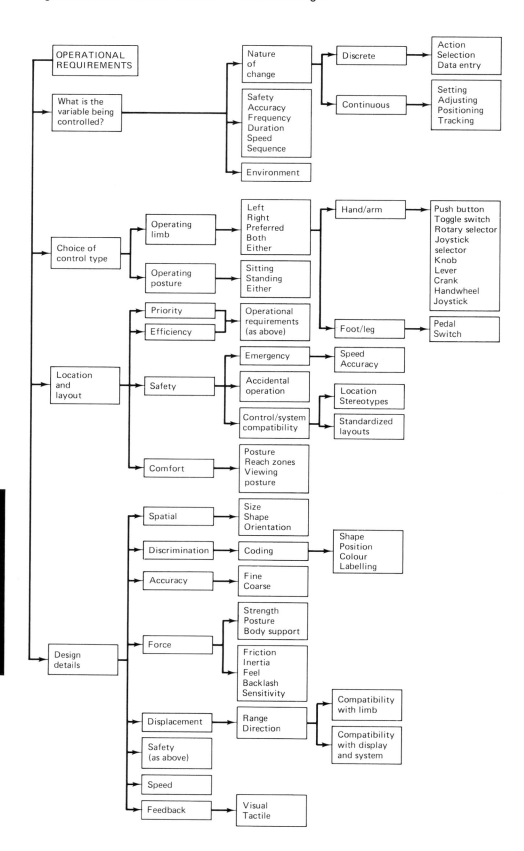

4.2. Choice of control type

Table 6. The general suitability of controls for different types of operation.

Control Type	High accuracy	High speed	Large force	Large displacement range	No. of discrete settings	High frequency of operation	Long duration of operation	Sequence	Visual identification	Non-visual identification	Check reading of position	Emergency action	Ease of compatibility with system response
Push button	—	H	—	—	2	H	L	H	L	L	L (Unless lit)	H	H
Toggle switch	—	H	—	—	2/3	M	L	M	M	H	H	H	L
Rocker switch	—	H	—	—	2/3	M	L	M	M	H	H	H	L
Rotary selector	H	H	—	—	3 – 24	M	L/M	M	M	M	M	M	H
Joystick selector	H	H	L	—	4 – 8	H	L	L	M	M	M	M	—
Cranks:													
Small	L	H	L	H	—	M	M	—	H	H	L	H	M
Large	H	L	H	H								L	
Horizontal	M	M	H	H									
Vertical	L	H	M	H									
Handwheels	H	L	L	L	—	M	M/H	—	H	M	L	L	M
	—	L	H	L									
Levers:													
Horizontal	L	H	L	L	—	M	M	M	M	M	H	M	L
Vertical (to/fro)	M	H	Short L	L								H	M
	M	H	Long H	L									
Vertical (across body)	M	M	M	—								M	L
Knob	M	—	—	M	—	M/L	M/L	H	M	M	L	—	M
	H		L	L									
Joystick	M	M	L	L	—	H	H	—	M/H	H	L	L	M
Pedals:													
Leg	M/L	M	H	—	—	M	M	L	—	M	—	H	M
Ankle	H	M/H	L	—	—	H	H	M	—	M	—	M	M
Footswitch	—	H	L	—	—	L	L	—	—	M	—	H	H

General suitability: H = High; M = Medium; L = Low; — = Unsuitable or not applicable
Note that high accuracy, high speed, large force and large displacement are generally incompatible.

4.3. Location and layout

4.3.1. General

Task requirements — Arrange for efficient, safe and comfortable operation according to priority, frequency, duration, force, speed, accuracy and sequence and other basic requirements.

Reach — Locate high priority controls in the high priority zone in front of the operator (see *Workspace design,* p. 13).

Limb — Divide between left and right hands and feet according to the need for simultaneous operation and variation in the preferred hand or foot (locate centrally for operation by right- or left-handed people).

Search — Controls to be in an expected or standardized layout with respect to each other.
More separation between hand controls is needed for 'blind' searching and location, to avoid accidental operation.

Compatibility — Controls must be in the same spatial layout as the system or displays.

Standardization (of layout, etc.) — Important where the operator moves between different machines, or where training is limited.

CONTROL

53

Consistency	Displays must be in a consistent location, and must move in a consistent (compatible) direction relative to their controls.
Location coding	By the position in relation to other controls, as well as by shape, size and texture.

4.3.2. Grouping

Avoid interference.
Arrange in order of priority.

Function

Arrange controls of similar function together (dissociate if confusion is likely).

Rows and columns

A maximum of three vertical columns and three horizontal rows.

4.3.3. Sequence

Sequential operations must flow smoothly.

Place sequential controls in close proximity. If the sequence never varies, incorrect responses can be eliminated by interlocking.

Where controls are sometimes omitted from the sequence use location coding.

Operate left to right and top to bottom.

4.3.4. Control – display relationships

Controls must be close to the appropriate displays *or* grouped in similar patterns.

Controls and appropriate displays or work must be operable/visible simultaneously without adopting an uncomfortable posture.

The left-hand control of a row of controls must refer to the top display of a column of displays, etc.

The smallest of a set of stacked knobs must refer to the left-hand display.
See also *Compatibility,* p. 53.

C
O
N
T
R
O
L

4.4. Design details

Figure 21. Design details of controls.

TYPICAL AND ALTERNATIVE SHAPES, AND RECOMMENDED DIMENSIONS (mm)	FORCE (kg)		DISPLACEMENT (mm)		NOTES
	MIN	MAX	MIN	MAX	

PUSH BUTTONS

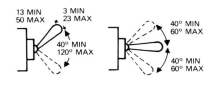

10 MIN
12-25 OPT
38-50 PALM
30 MIN GLOVES

50 RAD

SEPARATION (From other buttons)
15 MIN
22 MAX
130 NON-VISUAL

ALTERNATIVE SHAPES

Concave Rough
Non-slip

	FORCE MIN	FORCE MAX	DISPL. MIN	DISPL. MAX	NOTES
	0·25	1·2 (Frequent 0·8)	3	16 40 (Ball hand or gloves)	Size, shape and spacing depend on the consequence of error and operator skill.

Start with low resistance, build up, and then drop with click

Keyboards
0·15   0·3

For a sloping plane vertical buttons are preferred to buttons at 90° to the panel.

May include built-in illumination.

May require colour coding.

Barriers or recesses can be used for separation

TOGGLE SWITCHES

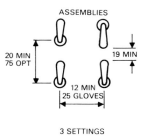

13 MIN
50 MAX

3 MIN
23 MAX

40° MIN
120° MAX

40° MIN
60° MAX

40° MIN
60° MAX

2 SETTINGS

ASSEMBLIES

20 MIN
75 OPT

19 MIN

12 MIN
25 GLOVES

3 SETTINGS

UK CONVENTION

OFF

OFF ⊙ ON

ON

ALTERNATIVE SHAPES

0·25   10   40° between settings

Spring loading near the central position. Resistance to build up, then fall off. No resting between settings.

ROCKER SWITCHES

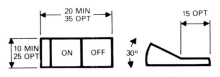

20 MIN
35 OPT

15 OPT

10 MIN
25 OPT

ON OFF

30°

Can be used instead of toggles. A legend is possible.

Figure 21 (cont.)

TYPICAL AND ALTERNATIVE SHAPES RECOMMENDED DIMENSIONS (mm)	FORCE (kg)		DISPLACEMENT (mm)		NOTES
	MIN	MAX	MIN	MAX	

ROTARY SELECTOR (KNOB OR ROTARY BAR)

KNOB

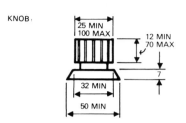

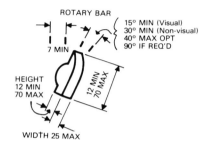

ROTARY BAR

15° MIN (Visual)
30° MIN (Non-visual)
40° MAX OPT
90° IF REQ'D

7 MIN

HEIGHT
12 MIN
70 MAX

12 MIN
70 MAX

WIDTH 25 MAX

ALTERNATIVE SHAPES

A skirt gives a more visible scale and prevents damage to scale.

Bar knobs are preferable for checking settings in an array.

30° detents can be identified by feel.

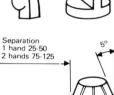

Separation
1 hand 25-50
2 hands 75-125

5°

25 max
13 min

10 min
100 max

0.44 N m (torque)

Higher torque if knurled or larger size.
Serrated edges for grip.

Unlimited (depends on operating time)

Unsuitable for rapid adjustment unless folding crank handle

STACKED
12 OPT

5°

20 OPT

20 OPT

6 MIN

44 OPT

74 OPT

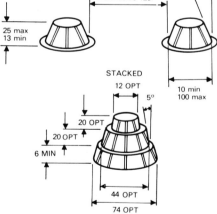

HIGH TORQUE (5 Finger grab)

Flutes
10 Min Rad

50 MIN
100 MAX

25

12-25

25 min

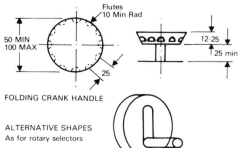

FOLDING CRANK HANDLE

ALTERNATIVE SHAPES
As for rotary selectors

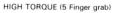

TYPICAL AND ALTERNATIVE SHAPES RECOMMENDED DIMENSIONS mm	FORCE (kg) MIN / MAX	DISPLACEMENT (mm) MIN / MAX	NOTES

CRANKS

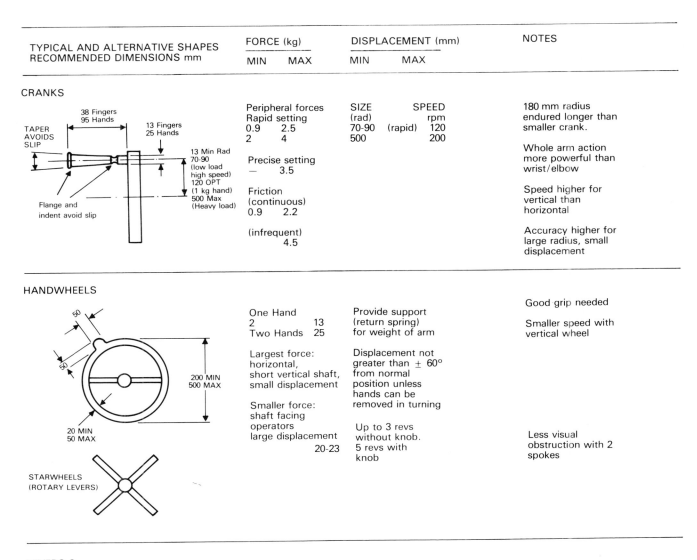

38 Fingers
95 Hands
13 Fingers
25 Hands

TAPER AVOIDS SLIP

13 Min Rad
70-90 (low load high speed)
120 OPT (1 kg hand)
500 Max (Heavy load)

Flange and indent avoid slip

FORCE (kg)
Peripheral forces
Rapid setting
0.9   2.5
2   4

Precise setting
—   3.5

Friction (continuous)
0.9   2.2

(infrequent)
4.5

DISPLACEMENT (mm)
SIZE (rad)	SPEED rpm
70-90 (rapid)	120
500	200

NOTES
180 mm radius endured longer than smaller crank.

Whole arm action more powerful than wrist/elbow

Speed higher for vertical than horizontal

Accuracy higher for large radius, small displacement

HANDWHEELS

50

200 MIN
500 MAX

20 MIN
50 MAX

STARWHEELS (ROTARY LEVERS)

FORCE (kg)
One Hand
2   13
Two Hands   25

Largest force: horizontal, short vertical shaft, small displacement

Smaller force: shaft facing operators large displacement
20-23

DISPLACEMENT (mm)
Provide support (return spring) for weight of arm

Displacement not greater than ± 60° from normal position unless hands can be removed in turning

Up to 3 revs without knob.
5 revs with knob

NOTES
Good grip needed

Smaller speed with vertical wheel

Less visual obstruction with 2 spokes

LEVERS & JOYSTICKS

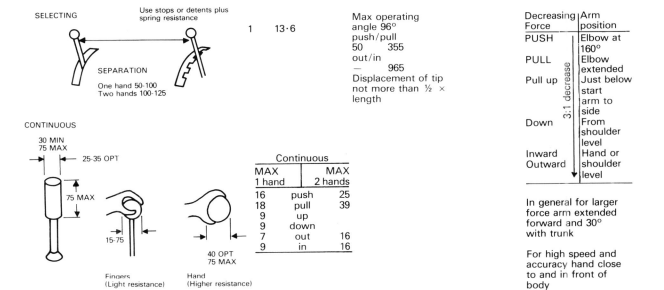

SELECTING

Use stops or detents plus spring resistance

1   13·6

SEPARATION
One hand 50-100
Two hands 100-125

CONTINUOUS

30 MIN
75 MAX
25-35 OPT
75 MAX

15-75

40 OPT
75 MAX

Fingers (Light resistance)
Hand (Higher resistance)

DISPLACEMENT (mm)
Max operating angle 96°
push/pull
50   355
out/in
—   965
Displacement of tip not more than ½ × length

Continuous		
MAX 1 hand		MAX 2 hands
16	push	25
18	pull	39
9	up	
9	down	
7	out	16
9	in	16

NOTES

Decreasing Force		Arm position
PUSH		Elbow at 160°
PULL	3:1 decrease	Elbow extended
Pull up		Just below start arm to side
Down		From shoulder level
Inward Outward		Hand or shoulder level

In general for larger force arm extended forward and 30° with trunk

For high speed and accuracy hand close to and in front of body

Figure 21 (cont.)

TYPICAL AND ALTERNATIVE SHAPES RECOMMENDED DIMENSIONS (mm)	FORCE (kg)		DISPLACEMENT (mm)		NOTES
	MIN	MAX	MIN	MAX	

HORIZONTAL

 or

ALTERNATIVE SHAPES

Handgrips
Straight grips for displacement < 30°

Ball grip for >30°

Overlap of finger and thumb for stronger grip

Aim for maximum contact area

FOOT PEDALS

LEG ACTUATED (BRAKE) TYPE   1·5   9

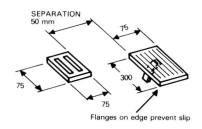

SEPARATION 50 mm
75
300
75
75
Flanges on edge prevent slip

NB approx 30% reduction in force 400mm below seat

150

Sitting operation for foot pedals

Standing permissible if pedal at floor level or infrequent, short duration operation. Provide support for weight of leg (return spring)

ANKLE ACTUATED (ACCELERATOR) TYPE

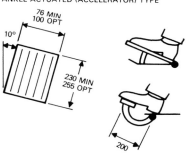

76 MIN
100 OPT
10°
230 MIN
255 OPT
200

1·5   5·4

(1·5 kg is spring return pressure)

Max force with knee at 160°
Leg forward of hips
Pivot at heel or in front of toe

Max accuracy with knee 95-135° and ankle 85-110°
Pivot between toe and arch

Higher accuracy and operating speed for close spacing

FOOT SWITCHES

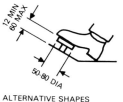

12 MIN
60 MAX
50-80 DIA

Return spring 8 kg for standing operation

Standing operation permissible

Treads avoid slip

ALTERNATIVE SHAPES

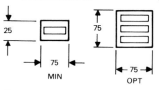

25
75
MIN
75
OPT
100
MAX

C
O
N
T
R
O
L

4.4.1. Further notes

Other types of control or variations on the above may be suitable for particular situations, e.g., slide switches, thumbwheels.

The above data are intended only to provide general guidelines for control selection and design, particularly that on forces. The characteristics and abilities of the proposed users and the task requirements must be considered throughout. In some cases control design will be limited by space, commercial availability, etc.

Performance characteristics depend greatly on the strength, fitness, skill and training of the operator, location of the control, direction and distance of movement, duration of the task, etc.

In allowing for strength variations, design for the weakest user (allow for age, sex, fitness, training).

Allow for the duration of the control task. An operator can only exert maximum strength for short periods, with long recovery periods: 10% of maximum strength can be exerted continuously and 20% frequently.

4.5. Control – machine relationships

4.5.1. General considerations

Controls are compatible when the machine (or display) moves in an expected direction relative to the control movement, *or* when the controls correspond spatially or functionally to the system being controlled.

Stereotyped movements may be:

In designing control directions consider:
Stereotypes.
Accepted practice.
Consistency.
Standardization.

Some consequences of poor compatibility are:
Reversion to expected direction under stress even if incompatibility has been learnt.
Longer training time.
More errors in the initial response.
Lower speed, precision, reaction time.
Marked effects with age.

Compatibility is especially important where:
Errors are dangerous or costly.
Operations are complex.
The sequence is interrupted.
Training is limited.
There are frequent changes of machine by an operator and non-standardized controls.

Consistency is important, especially where there is no strong stereotype or when laying out groups of controls and displays.

4.5.2. General rules

The top or left-hand side of the control should move with the display or machine action.

The side of the control nearest the display should move with the display or machine action.

The movement of the control should be proportional to the display or machine movement.

Display movements are according to the line of regard and not the orientation of the body.

Dominance varies with display position relative to the operator, but less so with strong stereotypes.

It is not affected by the preferred hand.

Figure 22. Required movement of control for movement of machine.

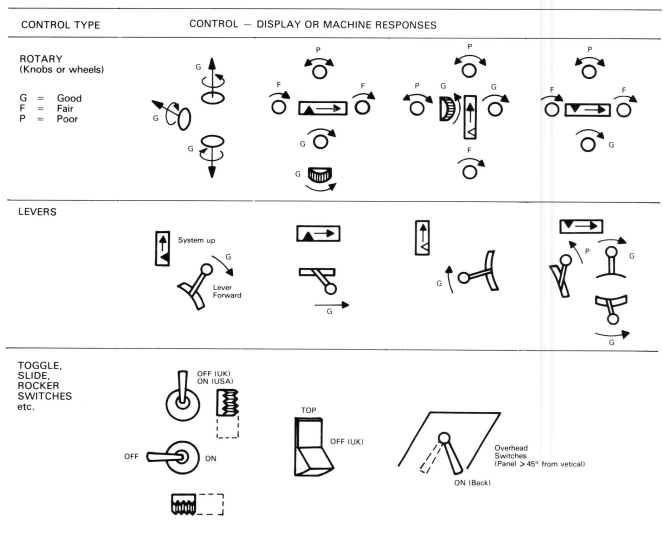

4.5.3. Feedback

Power assistance

For positional control, the machine moves a distance corresponding to the control shift.
For velocity control, the machine keeps moving at a velocity proportional to the movement of the control (this allows flexibility in design and improved performance).

C
O
N
T
R
O
L

4.5.4. 'Feel'

Resistance + kinaesthesis (sense of position and movement), e.g., spring loading, to indicate zero or a central postion.
NB. High resistance or small displacement masks the 'feel'.

4.5.5. Friction

Static friction

Opposes initial movement, which increases rapidly once it is overcome.

Coulomb friction

Continues to resist movement but does not change with amplitude or speed of displacement. It is useful for preventing accidental operation due to drift, tremor, jolting or weight of limb.

4.5.6. Elastic resistance

This increases with increase in displacement. The level of resistance is the primary cue to the level of control output (it can be nearly zero). It is often used in combination with displacement to provide a resistance gradient across the displacement range.
Elastic resistance is also called spring loading.

4.5.7. Viscous damping

This increases with an increase in the displacement speed. It is useful for controls which must be displaced at constant speed, and is most effective when used in combination with inertia, which increases with increase in displacement acceleration.

4.5.8. Pressure and amplitude feedback

$$\text{Combined change of sensation} = \frac{\text{Change of resistance}}{\text{Resistance} \times \text{displacement}} = \frac{\Delta F}{F(\Delta D)}$$

(i.e., it is a ratio of proportional change in resistance to change in location).

4.5.9. Sensitivity

To pressure

Less sensitivity to change at lower pressure.

To displacement

$$\text{Displacement ratio } R = \frac{\text{Distance moved by control or display}}{\text{Distance moved by machine}}$$

Small R is for large, rapid movements with low accuracy. Hunting is likely and skilled performance is difficult.
Large R is for fine control, but is slower.
A compromise is needed:

$$R > \frac{\text{Expected operator error}}{\text{Maximum acceptable machine positioning error}}$$

To velocity

The velocity of movement of the display or machine per unit displacement of control.

To gain

This should be balanced against machine lag.

5. Displays and Information

DISPLAYS / INFORMATION

5.1. Design criteria

Figure 23. Flow chart of criteria for the design of displays.

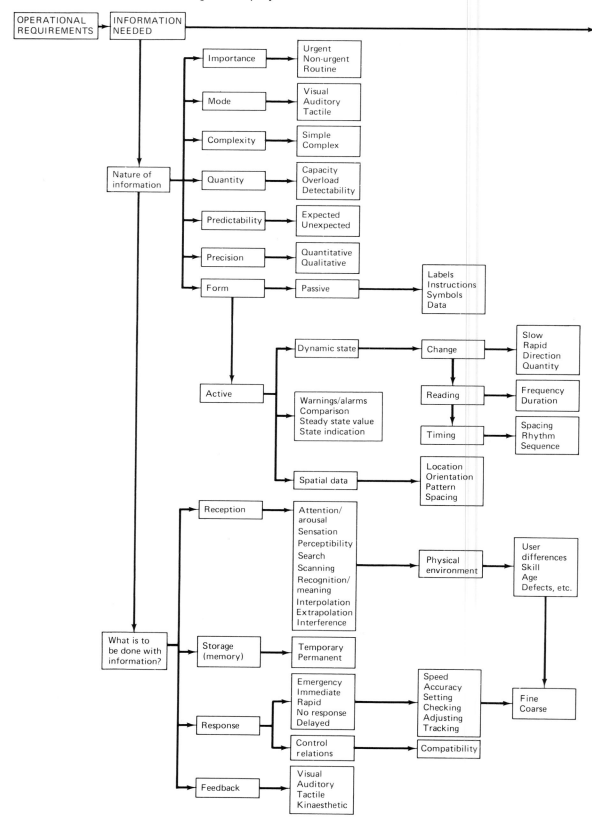

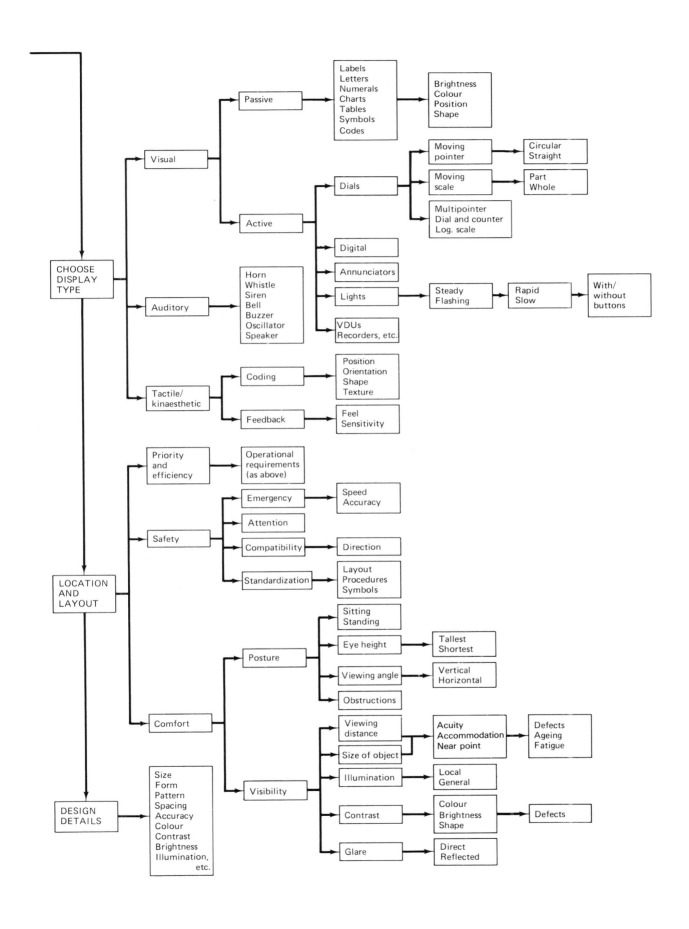

5.2. Choice of display type

5.2.1. General

Choose according to *Design criteria* (p. 64) and the considerations below.

Consider the nature of the information and what is to be done with it, paying particular attention to the difficulties of attending to sensing, interpreting (perception), memorising and responding to information.

Where attention is critical, two cues are better than one.

5.2.2. Lights

This includes illuminated buttons and colour coding.

Warnings/urgent messages: combine with an auditory alarm for gaining attention, flashing or steady.

Discrepancy: flashing light or steady, caution, etc.

Indication: steady.

Confirmation: command received.

Lights are useful for rhythmical information, ease of attention and search, recognition, discrimination and speed of response. With controls they are useful for checking and setting.

5.2.3. Dials

Dials are satisfactory for most information except warnings, and complex and stored information.

They may be used with controls for setting, etc.

Note the various types of dials:

Circular.
Sector.
Straight.
Linear and non-linear (avoid log. scales if possible).
Multi-pointer (avoid except for non-urgent information).
Moving scale (avoid except for non-urgent information).
Mixed dial + digital (for large ranges, high accuracy and direction of change).

Circular dials are better for comparison and rate of change.

Linear dials are better for compatibility and occupy less area for a given scale base.

Interpolation is difficult and errors are more likely with logarithmic scales.

5.2.4. Digital displays

These are used for high accuracy; slow change; quantitive information; frequent, short duration reading; and for setting machines.

They are unsuitable for rapid change or showing direction of change; and for check controlling, check reading or comparison, the position of the dial pointer is a useful visual cue.

Gross reading errors are more likely.

5.2.5. Annunciators

These are indicators or devices displaying a legend illuminated internally on receipt of an initiating signal. They are useful for non-quantitive, especially verbal, information, or for instructions or warnings.

5.2.6. Visual display units

VDUs are necessary for complex information outputs and data inputs.

See *Design criteria* (p. 64) for considerations relating to screen target or signal, visual workspace, etc.

5.2.7. Recording indicators

These are used where storage of information is required. (Note the limitations of human memory.)

5.2.8. Auditory displays

These are better for warnings and gaining attention, but should not distract or annoy. They should be of a suitable frequency and intensity for the environment.

They are useful for rapid change, rhythmical, spaced, infrequent information, ease of search and discrimination.

The signals are more easily remembered than visual signals, but are more easily interfered with (masked) by the environment.

Examples are horns, whistles, sirens, bells, buzzers, oscillators and speakers.

5.2.9. Other modes

Tactile (touch), kinaesthetic (movement), proprioceptive (position) and olfactory (smell) information may be useful in some systems.

5.2.10. Passive displays

Letters, numerals, charts, tables, symbols, codes and text may be used for warnings, labels, instructions, operating and maintenance procedures, settings, etc.

5.3. Location and layout

See also *Location and layout* (p. 53). Similar conditions apply.

5.3.1. Operational requirements

Arrange for efficient viewing and attention according to priority (frequency, duration, speed, accuracy, sequence) and importance for safety. High priority displays must be in the prime zone of vision.

5.3.2. Visibility

Arrange for comfortable vision: a comfortable posture and viewing angle for a range of users in a range of operating postures, seated or standing. Consider the priority of vision.

A comfortable viewing distance (e.g., 400 – 700 mm) for the size of object and environmental conditions is necessary.

The viewing angle must be approx. 90° to the line of sight and free from obstruction. Consider short and tall users.

Locate for maximum contrast and minimum glare (see CIBS Code, 1984).

Allow for visual and hearing defects and deterioration with age.

The display should be clearly and comfortably visible when the corresponding control is operated.

5.3.3. Search

Do not overcrowd or clutter — search time increases with display density.

Standardize the location of displays with respect to each other and the controls, but avoid too much regularity or irregularity.

5.3.4. Compatibility

See *Compatibility* (p. 53).

The movement and layout of displays must be compatible with the controls.

5.3.5. Coding

By position and colour do not use more than nine colours (see *Colour coding,* p. 75); or by labelling of suitable size and position. Do not obscure.

5.3.6. Grouping

Avoid interference.

Arrange in order of priority according to function.
Displays must be positioned close to the approriate controls *or* in a similar pattern.

5.3.7. Sequence

Arrange for a smooth sequence, i.e., in close proximity.

View from left to right and top to bottom.

5.3.8. Checking and comparison

If all pointers in a bank of dials are in the same position for steady state, the odd one out can easily be detected.

5.3.9. Graphic panels

These are useful for indicating flow and spatial systems diagonally.

Attention may be more difficult if they are spread over a large area, and if important and unimportant information is mixed.

5.4. Design details

5.4.1 Lights and illuminated buttons

Types

```
STEADY        WARNING
FLASHING      DISCREPANCY
              INDICATION        ILLUMINATED BUTTONS
              CONFIRMATION
```

Colour

See *Colour* (p. 72). Choose according to operational requirements, standards or local conventions.
Use filters/lenses according to BS 1376. Consider classification (A, B or special) and chromaticity.

Brightness

The brightness should command attention under all expected conditions without glare or dazzle.
Vary the size and brightness for extra distinguishability.
The signal brightness of white filters/lenses must be as for yellow.

Warnings

See *Alarms and warnings* (p. 73).
Include a standby lamp or power source in the event of failure (red).

DISPLAYS / INFORMATION

Discrepancy	Any discrepancy between the set position of an indicator and the operating conditions of the equipment causes the light to be illuminated (flashing if required). It may include a mimic diagram. An associated discrepancy controller may be so arranged that discrepancy is indicated when an operation is selected and cancelled when the operation is carried out (yellow).
Indication	Any specific or non-specific meaning, e.g., start (green), command confirmed (blue, white).
Flashing	Minimize the number. In general restrict to highest priority warnings. Other uses are: request attention, and to indicate a discrepancy or change in process. Rapid flashing should be used for higher priority (110 ± 30 flashes per minute) but note that flicker and flicker fusion may occur if the frequency is too high. Use slow flashing for lower priority (20 ± 5 flashes per minute).
Illuminated buttons	Never use for an emergency stop (the lamp may fail).

Indication

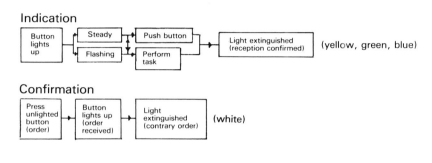

(yellow, green, blue)

Confirmation

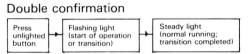

(white)

Double confirmation

Press unlighted button	Flashing light (start of operation or transition)	Steady light (normal running; transition completed)

5.4.2. Dial design	Refer to BS 3693, Parts I and II.
Accuracy	1% for 100 interpolated spacings.
Tolerance	Tolerance depends on the system or reading time. It must not be greater than the mechanical tolerance. It must be greater for the commercial than the test system.
Resolution	The resolution is the smallest fraction of the scale range to which the reading is made.
Called interval	This is the physical width or base angle into which scale divisions are divided with an eye to design tolerance.
Interpolation	Ten interpolations produces inaccuracy. Five interpolations are better than five marked divisions.
Dimensions	Scale base length $L = 7 \times 10^{-1.3}\, D$ (in mm). D = viewing distance. From this r can be determined by geometry. For example, the optimum diameter for $D = 600$ mm is $60-75$ mm.
	Allow for the poorest viewing conditions and the poorest eyesight.

DISPLAYS / INFORMATION

69

Figure 24. The design of dials.

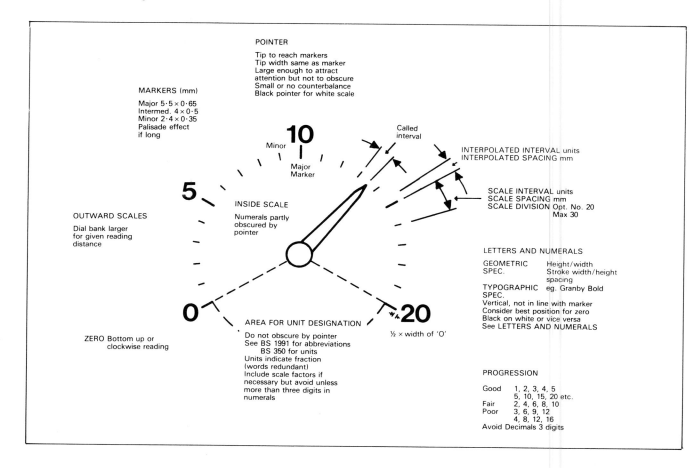

POINTER
Tip to reach markers
Tip width same as marker
Large enough to attract
attention but not to obscure
Small or no counterbalance
Black pointer for white scale

MARKERS (mm)
Major 5·5 × 0·65
Intermed. 4 × 0·5
Minor 2·4 × 0·35
Palisade effect
if long

Called
interval

INTERPOLATED INTERVAL units
INTERPOLATED SPACING mm

Minor **10**
Major
Marker

5

INSIDE SCALE
Numerals partly
obscured by
pointer

SCALE INTERVAL units
SCALE SPACING mm
SCALE DIVISION Opt. No. 20
Max 30

OUTWARD SCALES
Dial bank larger
for given reading
distance

LETTERS AND NUMERALS
GEOMETRIC   Height/width
SPEC.   Stroke width/height
              spacing
TYPOGRAPHIC eg. Granby Bold
SPEC.
Vertical, not in line with marker
Consider best position for zero
Black on white or vice versa
See LETTERS AND NUMERALS

0   **20**
½ × width of 'O'

ZERO Bottom up or
clockwise reading

AREA FOR UNIT DESIGNATION
Do not obscure by pointer
See BS 1991 for abbreviations
     BS 350 for units
Units indicate fraction
(words redundant)
Include scale factors if
necessary but avoid unless
more than three digits in
numerals

PROGRESSION

Good   1, 2, 3, 4, 5
        5, 10, 15, 20 etc.
Fair   2, 4, 6, 8, 10
Poor   3, 6, 9, 12
        4, 8, 12, 16
Avoid Decimals 3 digits

Refer to BS 3693 parts I and II
Dimensions in mm

SCALE BASE LENGTH
$L = 7 \times 10^{-1.3}D$ mm
D = Viewing Distance
Hence r by geometry
Size: optimum diameter 60 – 75 mm for D = 600 mm
Allow for the poorest viewing
conditions and poorest eyesight.

See calculations in BS 3693

Accuracy   1% for 100 interpolated spacings

Tolerance Depends on the system/reading time
           Must not be greater than the mechanical tolerance
           Must be greater for the commercial than the test
           system

Resolution Smallest fraction of scale range of
           which reading made

Called   Physical width or base angle into

Interval   which scale divisions divided by eye
           for distance tolerance

Interpo-   10 inaccurate
lation   5 interpolations better than 5 marked
           divisions

Other dial types

Straight scale

This has some compatibility advantages over a circular dial, e.g., the 12 o'clock effect where downward movement may be incompatible with upward movement of the control.

It occupies less area for a given scale base length then the circular dial.

Horizontal

Vertical

Sector

The markers should be opposite the pointer. Avoid the RH scale.

Top   Bottom
Horizontal

LH   RH
Vertical

Non-linear (log. scale)

Use for a large range. Avoid if possible. Use a digital display for a slow change, and digital plus pointer for a rapid change.

Use depends on accuracy and consequences of error. If it is used, interpolation should be constant.

Multi-pointer

Use for a large range. Avoid if possible — similar conditions to the log. scale apply (i.e., use digital displays). If used, the pointer and markers must be clearly distinguishable by varying size, thickness and colour.

Moving scale

Avoid except for crude measurements or where the consequences of error are not serious.

Mixed digital plus pointer

Use for large ranges where rapid change, high accuracy and the direction of change are required. Design the dial as above, the digits as below.

Table 7. The use of lights and colours in displays.

Colour	Steady indicator lights (clear lens or diffused light)	Flashing lights				Push buttons (surface colours as seen in incident white light)
		Rapid flash (110±30 flashes per minute)		Slow flash (20±5 flashes per minute)		
		Significance	On acceptance	Significance	On acceptance	
Red	Alarm Warning of potential danger Immediate action	Urgent action to avert danger (plus audible alarm)	Audible alarm (if any) silenced Flash signal changes to steady, extinguised with normal conditions Except for 'Danger' when flashing continues	N/A	N/A	Stop/off
Yellow	Caution Change or impending change	Action required Unwanted change (± audible alarm)	Audible alarm silenced Flashing signal may be extinguished or may continue flashing until action taken *or* may change to be steady signal	Lower priority Unwanted change	Flashing signal changes to steady	Intervention to suppress abnormal conditions or avoid unwanted change
Green	Safety Proceed Command confirmed	N/A	N/A	Changes of state Discrepancy from commanded state Attention required	Flashing signal changes to steady	Start/on General start Start part of machine Close switching device Inching/jogging
Blue	Specific meaning (any not covered by red/yellow/green Command confirmed	N/A	N/A	Changes of state Discrepancy from commanded state Attention required	Flashing signal changes to steady	Any specific meaning, e.g., reset
White	No specific meaning (neutral) Whenever doubt about red, etc. Command confirmed	Non-urgent action required, e.g., change of state or discrepency from commanded state	Audible alarm (if any) silenced. Flashing signal may be extinguished or may continue flashing until action taken *or* may change to a steady signal	Changes of state Discrepancy from commanded state Attention required	Flashing signal changes to steady	No specific meaning Start/on Reset Start/on and stop/off with the same button (better than red or green)
Black/ Grey	—	—	—	—	—	No specific meaning, e.g., inching/jogging (not red) Reset

5.4.3. Digital displays and annunciators

Digital displays

Use	See *Choice of type* (p. 66). For accurate, slow changing quantitative information.
Types	Electronic (LEDs) or mechanical counters (on drums). To BS requirements.
Colour	If non-BS colours are used, separate them from the standardized indicator lights and annunciators. Mechanical counters must be black on white or vice versa.

Brightness	There must be adequate visual contrast with the background. Avoid glare: surfaces must be matt or ground.
Numerals	See *Letters and numerals* (p. 76) and the appropriate standards. Spacing between characters: ≯ ½ × height. Stroke and width: 1/6 − 1/10 × height. Height: ≮ 1/360 × reading distance. Read from left to right.

Annunciators

Use	As an internally illuminated legend for conveying information, instructions or warnings.
Colour	See *Table 7.* Preferably use the colour on a dark background.
Illumination	Have adequate brightness but avoid glare or a halo (ground or matt surface). Use rear illumination with two or more parallel lamps for urgent annunciators.
Legend	The legend must not be visible until the lamp is lit. It must be clear and distinct.
Location	Locate according to the importance, and the number of operators who need to see it.
Dimensions	*Large size:* Spacing between window centres: vertical 50 mm horizontal 100 mm. Minimum illuminated window area: 40 × 90 mm. *Small size:* Spacing between window centres: vertical 25 mm horizontal 40 mm. Minimum illuminated window area: 20 × 33 mm.
Characters	As for digital displays numerals. Height to width ratio approx. 3:2 Use the abbreviations in BS 1991.

5.4.4. Lights (also auditory), alarms and warnings

Types	 See Choice of display type (p. 66)
Requirements	Ease of attention. Distinguishability. Rapid identification. Rapid response. See *Criteria* (pp. 64 − 65).
Visual	See *Table 7.*
Location	Locate in the prime zone of vision for easy attention and in compatible association with the control and control response (combine with the

control if possible).
See *Location and layout* (pp. 67 – 68).

Attention	Add an auditory signal where there is high urgency or where several displays must be monitored.
Identification	By colour coding (see *Table 7*). By labelling. Position at a distance from each other.
Flashing lights	Use only for the most important signals or in noisy environments (see *Lights,* p. 69).
Number of lights	Use as few as possible, e.g., use one main warning light plus a bank of indicators for more detailed information.
Brightness	The light should command attention under all conditions without glare. If external lighting is dimmed, dim with a photoelectric cell.

Auditory

Type	See *Choice* (p. 67). Choose according to importance, consequences of failure, whether action is required or not, and physical environment (e.g., background noise).
Location	Multi-directional — does not rely on visual attention or facing in particular direction. Some can be beamed directionally for greater effect (e.g., horn). Include a visual indication in the priority zone of the main panel and display more detailed information on a back-up panel. Locate according to hearing and attention requirements plus background noise. Note that sound intensity falls off with the square of the distance from the source.
Attention	Maximum alerting effect is caused by the sudden onset of high intensity sound. Variable frequency is more alerting than steady state.
Identification	If several sounds are used, clearly differentiate by quality of sound, frequency, and intensity (see *Choice,* p. 67).
Sound level	This must not be painful or damaging (see *Auditory environment,* p. 42). It must not be startling, distracting or annoying. If intensities are high, include at least two frequencies from the lower end of the spectrum. Allow for hearing loss of some users, especially at higher frequencies.
Failure of alarm	Incorporate an emergency power supply for the alarm system if necessary. Automatic rectification or standby to be included if the expense is justified.
Rectification/acknowledge-ment/silencing	No silencing until the danger over if it is a danger to personnel. If it is only a warning, it should be capable of being silenced on acknowledgement. If a fault is present, the silencing of an auditory alarm should not cancel a visual alarm until the fault is rectified. See *Lights and illuminated buttons* (pp. 68 – 69).
Reset	The alarm should automatically reset when the fault has been rectified. See *Lights and illuminated buttons* (pp. 68 – 69).

DISPLAYS / INFORMATION

5.4.5. Visual display units

The design of the visual environment for a VDU is influenced by the intensity and contrast of the screen, the rate at which the screen image is electronically replaced (refresh rate), and the need to maintain relatively close eye focus for long periods of time on the screen and working data.

General lighting is recommended at 200 – 300 lux, with local desk lighting (adjustable) for individuals.

Reflections in the screen must be avoided by:
Darker walls, etc. behind user;
Matt screen surface;
Individual tilt and rotate facility for each VDU;
No direct light on screen.

Glare must be avoided by:
No bright surfaces, lights or windows near the line of sight of the screen;
Adjustable window coverings;
Highly diffused room lights.
(See Cakir *et al.,* 1981; Anon, 1983).

5.4.6. Passive displays and visual coding: general

Design criteria

Figure 25. Flow chart for the design of symbols for machines.

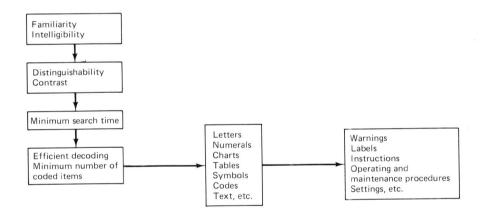

Coding types

Colour

Untrained users (inc. 'colour blind')	Equally discriminable colours	
Red	3R	Select
Orange	9R	those
Yellow	9YR	furthest
Blue	16Y	apart if
Purple	3G	less than
Grey	7BG	9 needed
Buff	9B	
White	9PB	
Black	3R	

Colour is best for rapid search, familiarity, contrast (black on white is best) etc.

A limited number of colours is preferable, ≯ 9, for untrained users.

The search time is much less if the colour of the target is known.

There is the problem of colour vision defects (mainly shortening of the red end of spectrum so that red appears as deep yellow).

Where appropriate add written or auditory information.

Consider the colour specification (CIE chromaticity value).

See *Bibliography* for Standards.

See *Lights and illuminated buttons* (pp. 68 – 69).

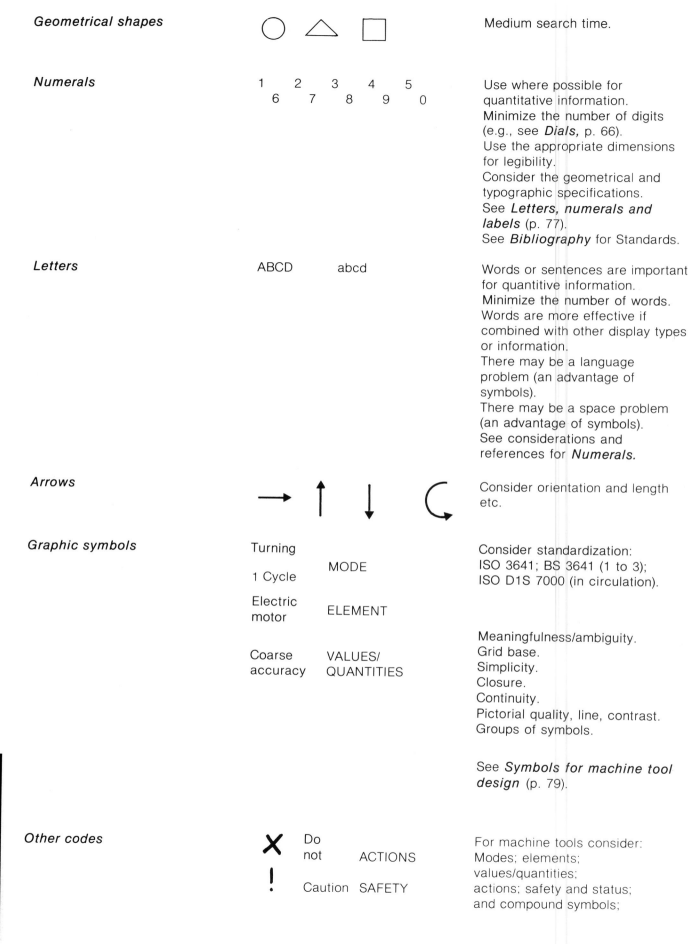

Geometrical shapes

Medium search time.

Numerals

1 2 3 4 5
6 7 8 9 0

Use where possible for quantitative information.
Minimize the number of digits (e.g., see *Dials,* p. 66).
Use the appropriate dimensions for legibility.
Consider the geometrical and typographic specifications.
See *Letters, numerals and labels* (p. 77).
See *Bibliography* for Standards.

Letters

ABCD   abcd

Words or sentences are important for quantitive information.
Minimize the number of words.
Words are more effective if combined with other display types or information.
There may be a language problem (an advantage of symbols).
There may be a space problem (an advantage of symbols).
See considerations and references for *Numerals.*

Arrows

Consider orientation and length etc.

Graphic symbols

Turning

1 Cycle   MODE

Electric motor   ELEMENT

Coarse accuracy   VALUES/ QUANTITIES

Consider standardization:
ISO 3641; BS 3641 (1 to 3);
ISO D1S 7000 (in circulation).

Meaningfulness/ambiguity.
Grid base.
Simplicity.
Closure.
Continuity.
Pictorial quality, line, contrast.
Groups of symbols.

See *Symbols for machine tool design* (p. 79).

Other codes

X   Do not   ACTIONS

!   Caution   SAFETY

For machine tools consider:
Modes; elements;
values/quantities;
actions; safety and status;
and compound symbols;

DISPLAYS/INFORMATION

Size	○　○　○	Search times are longer than for other codes. Standardize layouts where possible. Consider compatibility.
Position/Location		See *Location and layout* (p. 67).
Brightness	○　-○-　☼	This must not be excessively bright or dull. It must be brighter for more important displays. See *Lights* (p. 66).
Combinations	STOP — (STOP) — { STOP Colour Word Brightness	Better identification can be obtained if codes are combined.

5.4.7. Letters, numerals and labels

Design criteria

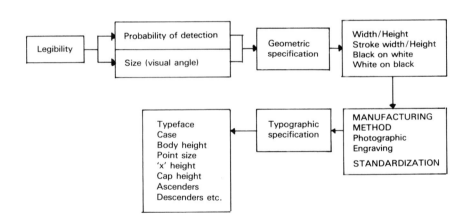

Geometric specification

Optimum width to height ration = 0·7:1
Stroke width to height ratio = 1:6 for black on white
                 = 1:8 for white on black
Optimum improved legibility and detection.

Typographic specification

Reinterpret the geometric specification and select a suitable typeface, e.g., Granby Bold numerals, Gill Sans letters (see BS 3693 Part I and BS 2961).
Use an ISO grid for standardization.
Compromise is necessary where space, manufacturing method or usage means that a particular typeface is unsuitable.

Labels   The aim is for easy search and identification in the poorest conditions.
                            Label controls, displays and other components using letters, numerals,
                            words, symbols, colour and other visual coding, as appropriate.
                            Use combinations of codes where possible for extra clarity.
                            Use a minimum number of words while retaining unambiguity.
                            Avoid redundancy and clutter.
                            Use standard abbreviations (BS 1991) and units (BS 350).
                            Design letters and numerals as indicated, to be of suitable size while
                            allowing for space and typographic restrictions.
                            Etching or embossing, etc., is more durable than painting.
                            Standardize the position and direction (horizontal not vertical).

5.4.8. Symbols: general principles

Application

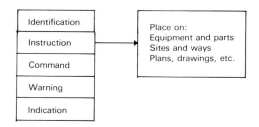

Design criteria

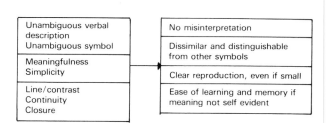

Design process   Identify the need for a symbol.
                              Define the purpose of the symbol — analyse operational
                              requirements.
                              Consider existing or proposed symbols.
                              Design, test and modify using the graphic form prescribed in ISO
                              3461.

Combined symbols   Symbols may be combined or grouped.
                              The meaning of the combination should be unambiguous (use as few
                              symbols as possible).

Graphic form/basic pattern Refer to ISO 3461.
                              The basic pattern is a frame of circles, squares, octagons, etc. to aid
                              designers in producing original designs. Forms of suitable line
                              thickness are laid out on this pattern.
                              Forms should be suitable for economic production by existing
                              techniques, e.g., engraving.
                              Other drawing aids, e.g., right angles and grids for aligning, are
                              described in ISO 3461.

Orientation of symbols   State explicitly if the meaning depends on orientation.

Colour   Generally black and white are sufficient.
                              Colour is specified in some cases.

5.4.9. Symbols for machine tool design

Design criteria   See *Symbols: general principles* (p. 78).

Standardization   Refer to ISO DIS 7000, ISO 3461, BS 3641 and ISO 369.
Use ISO and BSI standards as appropriate, except where the latter
have been superseded.
Note that some symbols (especially international ones) may be a
compromise between various requirements or may be of limited value
without training.

Types of symbol

Figure 26. Flow chart of the categories of symbols used in machine tool design.

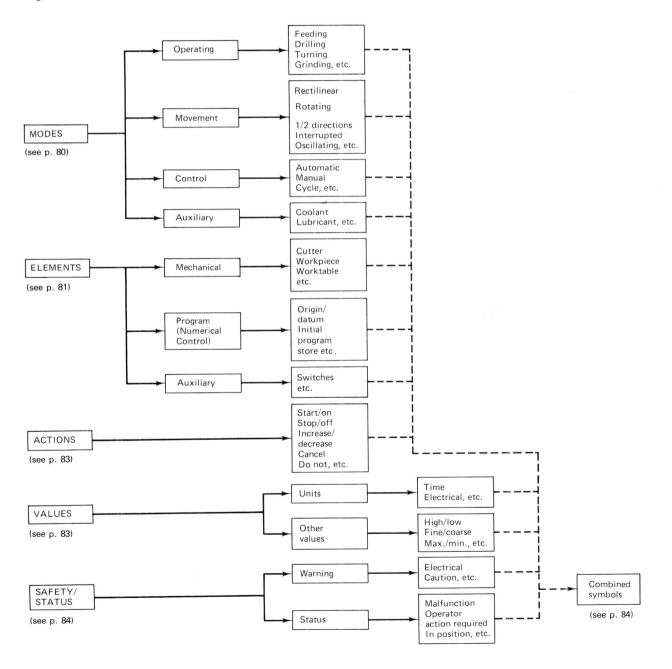

MODES

OPERATING MODES

Bending/folding

Blow

Boring

Broaching chain

Broaching external

Broaching internal

Copying

Drilling

Feed

Grinding

Grinding, cut-off

Grinding, external cylindrical

Grinding, face

Grinding, internal cylindrical

Grinding, plunge out

Honing

Lapping

OPERATING MODES (Cont.)

Milling, climb

Milling, conventional

Milling, vertical

Parting off

Planing

Reaming

Shearing/cutting

Tapping

Threading

Turning

MOVEMENT MODES

Dwell

Feed per stroke

Rectilinear motion

Rectilinear motion in two directions

Rectilinear motion, interrupted (jog)

Rectilinear motion, limited

Rectilinear motion, limited and return

Rectilinear motion oscillating

Rapid traverse

MOVEMENT MODES (Cont.)

Rotation in two directions

Rotation, continuous direction

Rotation, interrupted

Rotation, limited

Rotation, limited and return

Rotation, oscillating

CONTROL MODES

Automatic

Magnetic

Manual

Multi-man operation

One cycle

Step-cycle

AUXILIARY MODES

Balance, dynamic

Balance, static

Blowing unit

DISPLAYS/ INFORMATION

80

Coolant flood	
Coolant mist	
Draining	
Dressing, crush	
Dressing, face	
Dressing, form	
Dressing, truing	
Electrical instruction manual or diagram	
Filling	
Gauge size, external	
Gauge size, internal	
Hydraulic	
Lubricant, grease	
Lubricant, oil	
Maintenance	
Material feed	
Out of balance	
Refer to instruction book	
Suction unit	
Ventilate blow die	

Wall thickness of a preform	
Work area illumination	

ELEMENTS

MECHANICAL ELEMENTS

Abrasive wheel	
Bleed point	
Blow mandrel	
Blow moulding die	
Blow needle	
Broach	
Broach puller	
Broach retriever	
Cam	
Chain (transmission)	
Chuck	
Clamp	
Clutch	
Collet	
Conveyor	
Cutter (general symbol)	
Cutter block	
Cutter block (alternative symbol)	
Drive, belt	
Drive, gear	
Filter	
Fixture	

DISPLAYS/ INFORMATION

81

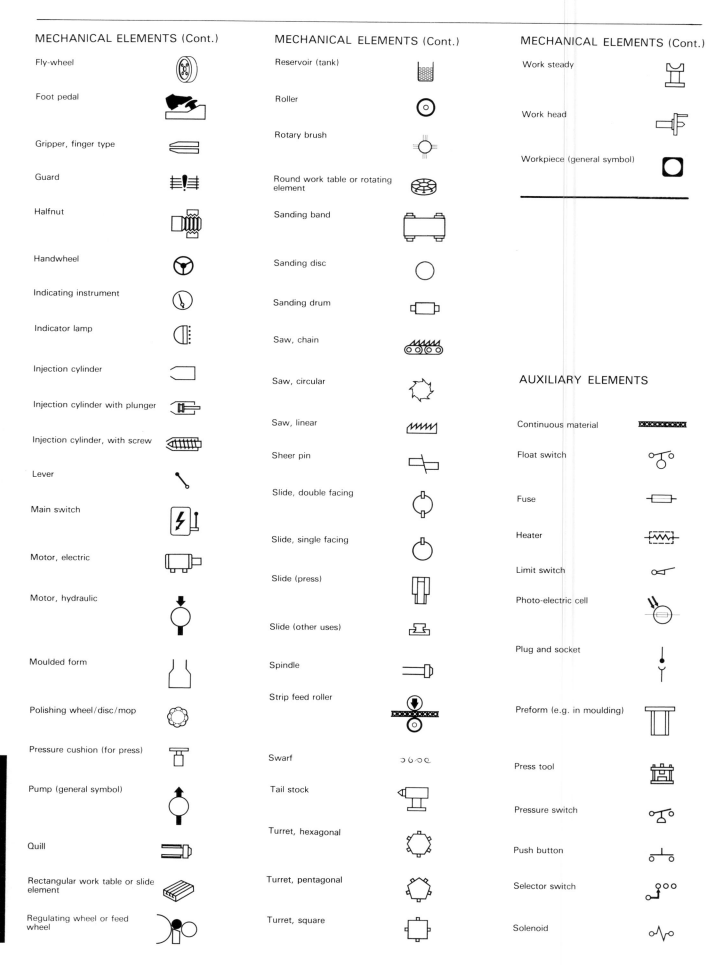

MECHANICAL ELEMENTS (Cont.)

Fly-wheel

Foot pedal

Gripper, finger type

Guard

Halfnut

Handwheel

Indicating instrument

Indicator lamp

Injection cylinder

Injection cylinder with plunger

Injection cylinder, with screw

Lever

Main switch

Motor, electric

Motor, hydraulic

Moulded form

Polishing wheel/disc/mop

Pressure cushion (for press)

Pump (general symbol)

Quill

Rectangular work table or slide element

Regulating wheel or feed wheel

MECHANICAL ELEMENTS (Cont.)

Reservoir (tank)

Roller

Rotary brush

Round work table or rotating element

Sanding band

Sanding disc

Sanding drum

Saw, chain

Saw, circular

Saw, linear

Sheer pin

Slide, double facing

Slide, single facing

Slide (press)

Slide (other uses)

Spindle

Strip feed roller

Swarf

Tail stock

Turret, hexagonal

Turret, pentagonal

Turret, square

MECHANICAL ELEMENTS (Cont.)

Work steady

Work head

Workpiece (general symbol)

AUXILIARY ELEMENTS

Continuous material

Float switch

Fuse

Heater

Limit switch

Photo-electric cell

Plug and socket

Preform (e.g. in moulding)

Press tool

Pressure switch

Push button

Selector switch

Solenoid

AUXILIARY ELEMENTS (Cont.)

Switch

Thermostat

Transformer

ACTIONS

Adjustable

Air eject moulded form

Brake off

Brake on

Disengage

Emergency return of automatic cycle to start

Emergency stop

Engage

In

In action as long as control operated

Lock or tighten

Out

Start and stop with same control

Start/on

Stepless regulation

Stop/off

Trim moulded form

Unlock or untighten

Value, decrease

Value, increase

Work weightpiece

VALUES

QUANTITIES

Amperes

Diameter

Hertz

High

Increment

Low

One revolution

Revolutions

Temperature

Time, hours

Time, minutes

Time, seconds

Volts

Watts

Weight

DISPLAYS/INFORMATION

SAFETY AND STATUS INDICATIONS

WARNINGS

Attention — electrical danger

Change speed in motion only

Change speed in stopped position only

Caution

STATUS INDICATIONS

A.C. supply

D.C. supply

Earth

Malfunction

COMBINED SYMBOLS

MECHANICAL SYMBOLS

Blade clearance

Blade tensioning adjusting

Broach cutting starter

Broach force

Broach return stroke

Broaching, automatic

Broaching, workpiece feeding

Close gripper

Close or lock puller head (broaching machine)

Cutter hold

Cutter release

Direction of spindle rotation

Ejector bar adjustment

Feed per minute

xmm/min

Feed per revolution

xmm/$\circlearrowright$

Feed, longitudinal

Feed, normal

$\frac{1}{1}$

MECHANICAL SYMBOLS (Cont.)

Feed, rapid

$\frac{x}{1}$

Feed, reduce

$\frac{1}{x}$

Feed, transverse

Feed, vertical

Halfnut, close

Halfnut, open

Indexing of circular table

Interchange grinding wheels

Interchange table

Level, full

Level, low

Load broach into puller

Number of revolutions per minute (spindle speed)

x$\bigcirc$/min

Open or unlock retriever (broaching machine)

Peripheral speed of drill

xmm/min

Peripheral speed of milling cutter

xmm/min

Pressure cushion compressed

Pressure cushion gripping

Pump, coolant

Pump, hydraulic system

DISPLAYS / INFORMATION

MECHANICAL SYMBOLS (Cont.)

Pump, lubricant

Shut height (refer to press)

Shuttle table

Slide adjustment

Slide load force (presses)

Speed of boring cut

xmm/min

Speed of planing cut

xmm/min

Speed of turning cut

xmm/min

Stroke adjustment

Tilting table

Tracer, disengage

Tracer engage

Wheel positioning

Work, load

Work, unload

Workpiece conveyor

NUMERICAL CONTROL SYMBOLS

MACHINE TOOL SYMBOLS

Absolute program (co-ordinate dimension words)

Actual position

Axis control in mirror image mode (machine program)

Axis control, normal (machine follows program)

Backward search for beginning of program without machine functions

Backward search for block number without machine functions

Backward search for particular data without machine functions

Backward search for program alignment function without machine functions

Backward tape wind without data read without machine functions

Battery

Beginning of program

Block (basic symbol)

Buffer storage

Cancel, delete (basic symbol)

Compensation or offset (basic symbol)

Co-ordinate basic origin

Data carrier (basic symbol)

Data carrier fault

Data carrier input via an alternative device

Delete store contents

MACHINE TOOL SYMBOLS (Cont.)

Do not (basic symbol)

Editing data in storage

End of program

End of program with automatic rewind to beginning of program without machine functions

Forward block by block read all data with machine functions

Forward continuous read all data without machine functions

Forward continuous read all data with machine functions

Forward continuous read all data with machine functions

Forward search for block number without machine functions

Forward search for particular data without machine functions

Forward search for program alignment function without machine functions

Forward tape wind without data read without machine functions

Grid point (sub-reference position)

In position

Incremental program (incremental dimension words)

Interchange (basic symbol)

Manual data input

Modify, amend, edit (basic symbol)

Optional block skip

Origin/datum (basic symbol)

Positioning accuracy — coarse

Positioning accuracy — fine

85

MACHINE TOOL SYMBOLS (Cont.)

Positioning accuracy
— normal

Position error (Servo error)

Prewarning storage
overflow

Program data error

Program edit

Program from external
device

Program storage

Program with machine
functions (basic symbols)

Program without machine
functions (basic symbol)

Programmed position

Programmed optional stop
with machine functions

Programmed stop
with machine functions

Read data from store

Reference position

Repositioning

Reset (basic symbol)

Reset store contents

Store (basic symbol)

Storage error

Storage overflow

Subroutine

Subroutine storage

MACHINE TOOL SYMBOLS (Cont.)

Tool diameter
compensation (rotating
tool)

Tool length compensation
(rotating tool)

Tool offset (non-rotating
tool)

Tool radius compensation
(rotating tool)

Tool tip radius
compensation

Write data into store

Zero offset

ADDITIONAL SYMBOLS

Continuous path

Display

Do not

End point of circle

Magazine

Maximum

Minimum

Null

Operator action
required
Examine, check

Oriented stop

Per cent %

Planetary milling

Plugboard

Point-to-point

Restart after
optional stop

Tool fault,
e.g. missing tool

Tool store

Verified

Groups of symbols

Symbols may be combined to form new compound symbols as follows with new meanings (number of symbols should be minimized to avoid ambiguity).

The new combined symbol may be a   Mode
Element
Value/quantity
Action
Warning or status

Slide balance pressure

Combined symbols may be used in direct association with controls and are then of the following form (see BS 3641 for examples; see also *Instruction plates,* below).

Figure 28. Symbol elements.

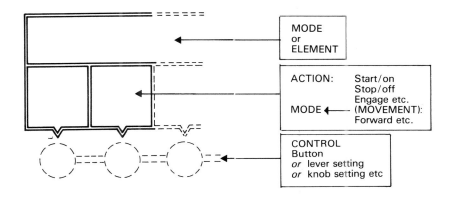

5.4.10. Instruction plates

Aims and criteria

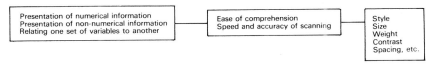

The plate may or may not be associated with controls and displays. See also *Criteria for visual coding* (p. 75), *Letters and numerals* (p. 77), and *Labels and symbols* (p. 78).

Presentation methods

Sentences

Use the following methods singly, or in appropriate combinations.

Avoid prose in bureaucratic style where information must be easily understood.
Keep sentences short, but do not telegraph so that the meaning is lost.
Present lists of simple sentences with appropriate sub-headings where information must be remembered.
Avoid jargon if simpler words will suffice.
Avoid redundant words and information.
Use standard (BS 1991) and clear abbreviations.

Logic trees	Use where the user may be uncertain or need help in finding or using information.
	Use for trouble shooting.

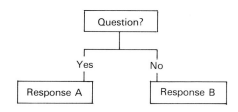

Symbols	Use standard symbols where possible. They are useful where language is a problem, where space is limited and where rapid comprehension is needed (see *Symbols,* pp. 79 – 86).
	They are particularly important for use in tables of control settings.
	Locate the symbols next to the appropriate controls (see *Combined symbols,* p. 84, and *Groups of symbols,* p. 87).
Illustration	Use where possible for clarity and to avoid technical jargon.
Tables	Tables are preferable to other methods if the user knows what to look up (faster and fewer errors).
	They are used for relating one set of variables to another, e.g., machine settings.
	They give a systematic arrangement of numerical and non-numerical information.
	Full, direct (explicit) presentation is preferred.
	This can be linear (list) or 2-dimensional (matrix).
	Scanning only is required.
	Avoid inferences or combinations of information from various parts of the table (implicit).

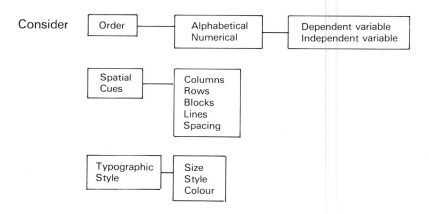

See also *Criteria* (p. 87).

DISPLAYS / INFORMATION

5.4.12. Tabular display design

Order

Position the machine variable to the right of the operating variable (read left to right).
Arrange the operating variable in numerical order to decrease downwards in column.
Use space/lines to facilitate horizontal/vertical scanning.

	$\curvearrowright$ min^{-1}		m min^{-1}	
Block or group	1850	DH	0.3	KT62
	1277	CH	0.4	KS12
	875	BH	0.5	KS32

Numerical decrease ↓

Operating (independent) variable — Machine (dependent) variable

Read left to right →

Spatial cues

Use spaces to group into threes or fives.
Groups of 10 are unsatisfactory but better than no group.
Minimize the space between paired items in adjacent columns (minimize the alignment error).
Vertical rules are to separate only unrelated variables in adjacent columns.
Omit redundant abbreviations within the table, e.g., units.
Omit landmarks or extra information within columns, especially where larger/bolder type can be used.

Typography

8 – 12 point 'x' height is recommended.
Dependent and independent variables must be the same typeface but differently weighted, e.g., the independent variable must be heavier in colour (see *Letters, numerals and labels,* p. 77).

Location of instruction plates

Consider design criteria in the location and layout of displays.
Locate the instruction plate close to the appropriate controls, setting or other operation so that instructions and work, controls etc. can be viewed/operated simultaneously (avoid the need to memorize information, or adopt an uncomfortable posture to see the instructions, etc.).
Instructions should not be obscured by materials, covers, components, dirt, etc.

Technical manuals

Similar conditions apply to the design of technical manuals for operation or maintenance.
See BS 4884 Parts I and II (1973), 'Specification for technical manuals', or any guide for writing manuals or instructions.

DISPLAYS / INFORMATION

89

Bibliography

Anon, 1974, *Applied Ergonomics Handbook* (London: IPC Science & Technology).

Anon, 1979, International anthropometric data, *Ergonomics Abstracts* **11.**

Bell, C. R., 1974, *Men at Work* (London: George Allen & Unwin).

Booth, B., 1967, Technical considerations in selecting handwheels for machine tools, *MTIRA Research Report No. 27.*

BS 1991, 1964, *Letters, Symbols, Signs and Abbreviations* (London: British Standards Institution). Superseded by BS 5775.

BS 2771, 1970, *Electrical Equipment of Machine Tools MA4: Valve Handwheels* (London: British Standards Institution).

BS 2961, 1967, *Typeface Nomenclature and Classification* (London: British Standards Institution).

BS 3042, 1971, *Standard Test Fingers and Probes for Checking Protection against Electrical, Mechanical and Thermal Hazard* (London: British Standards Institution).

BS 3378, See ISO 3864.

BS 3641, Part 1, 1971, *Symbols for Machine Tools* (London: British Standards Institution).

BS 3641, Part 3, 1973, *Symbols for Machine Tools* (London: British Standards Institution).

BS 3641, Part 2, 1980, *Specification for Machine Tools,* (London: British Standards Institution).

BS 3693, Part 1, 1964, *Design of Scales and Indexes. Instruments for Bold Presentation and Rapid Reading* (London: British Standards Institution).

BS 3693, Part II, 1969, *Design of Scales and Indexes. Indicating Instruments to be Read to* $0 \cdot 33 - 1 \cdot 25\%$ *Resolution* (London: British Standards Institution).

BS 4099, Parts I and II, 1970, *Colours for Indicator Lights, Push Buttons, Flashing Lights, Annunciators and Digital Readouts* (London: British Standards Institution).

BS 4884, Part I, 1973, *Specification for Technical Manuals* (London: British Standards Institution).

BS 4884, Part II, 1974, *Specification for Technical Manuals* (London: British Standards Institution).

BS 5304, 1975, *Safeguarding of Machinery* (London: British Standards Institution).

BS 5775, Parts 1, 2, 3, 4, 7, 11, 1979, *Quantities, Units and Symbols* (London: British Standards Institution).

BS 5775, Parts 0, 6, 8, 9, 10, 12, 13, 1982, *Quantities, Units and Symbols* (London: British Standards Institution).

BS 5775, Part 5, 1980, *Quantities, Units and Symbols* (London: British Standards Institution).

BSI, annual, *British Standards Yearbook* (London: British Standards Institution).

Burns, W., 1973, *Noise and Man* (London: John Murray).

CIBS, 1984, *Code for Interior Lighting* (London: Chartered Institution of Building Services).

Damon, A., Stoudt, H. W. & McFarland, R. A., 1966, *The Human Body in Equipment Design* (Cambridge, Mass.: Harvard University Press).

Diffrient, Tilley, Bardagjy, Henry Dreyfuss Associates, 1974, *Humanscale 1/2/3* (Cambridge, Mass.: MIT Press).

DIN 31001, Part I, 1983, *Safety Distances for Adults and Children* (Berlin: Deutsches Institut für Normung).

Easterby, R. S., 1970, The perception of symbols for machine displays, *Ergonomics* **13**, 149 – 158.

Fanger, P. O., 1970, *Thermal Comfort: Analysis and Applications in Environmental Engineering* (Copenhagen: Danish Technical Press).

Her Majesty's Factory Inspectorate, 1971, Noise and the worker, *Health and Safety at Work Reports No. 25* (London: HMSO).

Her Majesty's Factory Inspectorate, 1978, Lighting in offices, shops and railway premises, *Health and Safety at Work Reports No. 39* (London: HMSO).

Hopkinson, R. G. & Collins, J. B., 1977, *The Ergonomics of Lighting* (London: Macdonald Technical Scientific).

IEC, 1973, *Preferred Colour Coding for Indicator Lamps* (Geneva: International Electrotechnical Commission).

IES, 1977, *Code For Interior Lighting* (London: Illuminating Engineering Society) now superseded by CIBS Code, 1984.

IES, 1983, *The New IES Code* (London: Chartered Institution of Building Services, Lighting Division).

ISO 369, 1964, *Symbols for Indications on Machine Tools* (Geneva: International Standards Organisation).

ISO 3461, 1976, *Graphic Symbols: General Principles for Presentation* (Geneva: International Standards Organisation).

ISO 3864, 1966, *Safety Colours and Safety Signs* (Geneva: International Standards Organisation).

ISO DIS 7000, 1978, *Graphic Symbols* (Geneva: International Standards Organisation).

ISO, annual, *International Standards Organisation Directory* (Geneva: International Standards Organisation).

Jones, J. C., 1963, Anthropometric data, limitations in use, *Architects Journal Information Library*, 6 Feb, 317–325.

Morgan, C. T., Cook, J. S., Chapanis, A. & Lund, M. W., 1963, *Human Engineering Guide to Equipment Design* (New York: McGraw-Hill).

NIOSH, 1981, *Work Practices Guide for Manual Lifting* (Cincinnati, Oh.: National Institute of Occupational Safety and Health).

Singleton, W. T., 1974, *Man–Machine Systems* (Harmondsworth, UK: Penguin).

Snook, S. H., 1978, The design of manual handling tasks, *Ergonomics* **21,** 963–985.

Van Cott, H. P. & Kinkade, R. G. (eds.), 1972, *Human Engineering Guide to Equipment Design* (Washington, D.C.: US Government Printing Office).

Whitfield, D., 1971, British Standards and ergonomics, *Applied Ergonomics* **2,** 238–242.

Wright, P., 1971, Writing to be understood: why use sentences? *Applied Ergonomics* **2,** 207–209.

Wright, P. & Fox, K., 1970, Presenting information in tables, *Applied Ergonomics* **1,** 232–242.

Index